PRENTICE-HALL CHEMISTRY SERIES

Kenneth S. Pitzer, Editor

**SYNTHETIC
INORGANIC
CHEMISTRY**

William L. Jolly
ASSOCIATE PROFESSOR OF CHEMISTRY
UNIVERSITY OF CALIFORNIA, BERKELEY

Synthetic

Inorganic

Chemistry

Prentice-Hall, Inc.
ENGLEWOOD CLIFFS, NEW JERSEY

Current printing (last digit):
12 11 10 9 8 7 6 5 4 3

© 1960 by *PRENTICE-HALL, Inc.*,
Englewood Cliffs, New Jersey

Library of Congress Catalog Card Number: 60–14660

PRINTED IN THE UNITED STATES OF AMERICA

88007–C

PREFACE

If there are few synthetic inorganic chemists in the United States today, it is surely not because of a lack of individuals with inherent talent, but rather because of an educational system that tends to accept the illusion that there are no new kinds of compounds to be discovered. Oddly enough, some of the main offenders are college-curriculum laboratory courses in "inorganic preparations." These courses usually consist of little more than the cook-book preparation of a series of rather prosaic compounds. When such courses are accompanied by lectures, the lecture material is often only remotely related to the laboratory work; the theoretical principles of synthesis are seldom discussed. The tedium and purposelessness of such courses has probably turned many good students away from careers in synthetic inorganic chemistry.

The main purpose of a course in inorganic preparations should be to awaken synthetic talents in students. The student should be taught both theoretical principles and laboratory technique. He should prepare unusual, "exotic" compounds that may spark his curiosity and make him wonder about non-existent compounds.

The laboratory work of a course in synthetic inorganic chemistry is influenced by the scholastic attainment of the students, the available time and equipment, and the desires of the instructor. The laboratory course outlined in Chapter 6 has been successfully taught to undergraduates at the University of California for four years. It is hoped that instructors at other institutions will find some novel and useful features in this course outline and will not hesitate to send in their suggestions and criticisms.

It is a pleasure to acknowledge the assistance of Professor Thomas Wartik, who read and commented upon the original manuscript, and of my wife, Frances, who improved much of the diction therein.

William L. Jolly

v

Contents

SYNTHETIC
INORGANIC
CHEMISTRY

CHAPTER I

INTRODUCTION

The Preparation of New Compounds

Why do chemists prepare new compounds?[1] This question may seem inappropriate in a book whose main purpose is to describe *how* chemists prepare new compounds. In fact, devotees of pure research may well consider the question irrelevant and trivial. However, it must be remembered that this book is primarily addressed to students who have not yet engaged in pure research and who have not enjoyed the thrill of original discovery. For these students it is necessary to justify any scientific endeavor, particularly one as little practiced as inorganic synthesis.

DISCOVERY THROUGH CURIOSITY

Curiosity led Alfred Stock to the discovery of an entirely new class of compounds: the boron hydrides and their derivatives. Stock has stated[2] that in 1912 he chose to study the boron hydrides because he felt that boron, the neighbor of carbon in the periodic system, might be expected to form a much greater variety of interesting compounds than merely boric acid and the borates, which were almost the only ones known at that time. But Stock probably never dreamed that, in the next twenty years, he and his co-workers would prepare such an extensive and fascinating series of compounds as is

[1] Some of the material in this chapter first appeared in *J. Chem. Education*, **36**, 513 (1959).

described in his monograph, "Hydrides of Boron and Silicon."[2] Some of these compounds are listed in Table 1.1. In retrospect, Stock stated, "The chemistry of boron has proved unexpectedly rich in results and many-sided in character although, just as in the case of silicon, the mobile portion of its chemistry is confined to the laboratory. In nature boron's dominating affinity for oxygen restricts it to the monotonous role of boric acid and the borates and prevents it from competing with carbon, its neighbor in the periodic system."[2] One is led to wonder what chemistry would be like in a world without an oxygen-containing atmosphere.

TABLE 1.1

Some Compounds Discovered by Stock and His Co-workers

Name	Formula	Skeletal structure

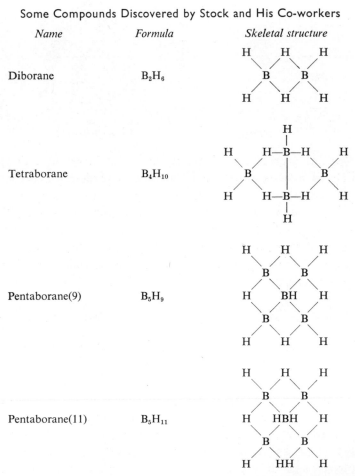

Diborane	B_2H_6	
Tetraborane	B_4H_{10}	
Pentaborane(9)	B_5H_9	
Pentaborane(11)	B_5H_{11}	

[2] A. Stock, "Hydrides of Boron and Silicon," Cornell University Press, Ithaca, N.Y., 1933.

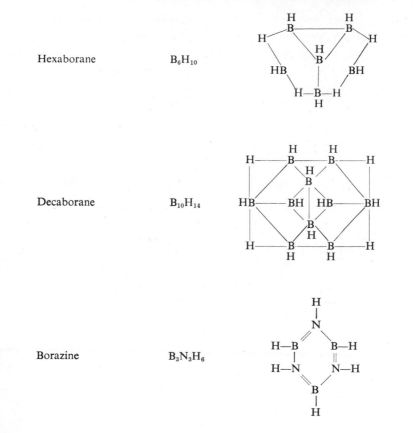

Hexaborane	B_6H_{10}	
Decaborane	$B_{10}H_{14}$	
Borazine	$B_3N_3H_6$	

"ACCIDENTAL" DISCOVERY

Simple chance, coupled with astute observation, has been responsible for the discovery of many new compounds. Oftentimes in the course of what is thought to be a straightforward synthesis or investigation, something completely unexpected happens. Perhaps a precipitate forms, a gas is evolved, a reaction mixture turns an unusual color, or a yield of expected product is very low. Unfortunately, the average chemist usually ignores such phenomena and goes on to work he can understand. But the curious chemist tries to find out what "went wrong" and in the process usually makes a significant —sometimes a spectacular—discovery.

Let us consider the unsuccessful, yet famous, attempt of Kealy and Pauson[3] to prepare dihydro-fulvalene (dicyclopentadienyl). These investigators tried to prepare this compound by the oxidation of cyclopenta-

[3] T. J. Kealy and P. L. Pauson, *Nature*, **168**, 1039 (1951).

dienylmagnesium bromide by ferric chloride, since the corresponding oxidation of phenylmagnesium bromide gives good yields of diphenyl:

$$6 \ C_6H_5MgBr + 2 \ FeCl_3 \longrightarrow 3 \ C_6H_5-C_6H_5 + 2 \ Fe$$
$$+ 3 \ MgBr_2 + 3 \ MgCl_2 \quad (1)$$

However, they obtained no dihydro-fulvalene. Instead, they isolated a remarkably stable organo-iron compound, which they identified as bis(cyclopentadienyl)iron(II). In their reaction, the ferric chloride presumably was first reduced to ferrous chloride by the Grignard reagent and the following reaction then took place:

$$2 \ C_5H_5MgBr + FeCl_2 \longrightarrow C_5H_5FeC_5H_5 + MgBr_2 + MgCl_2 \quad (2)$$

Later studies showed the bis(cyclopentadienyl)iron(II) ("ferrocene") to have the illustrated "sandwich" type of structure.

Soon after this discovery, better synthetic methods were developed for preparing ferrocene; and analogous compounds containing titanium, vanadium, chromium, manganese, cobalt, nickel, and ruthenium were prepared.[4]

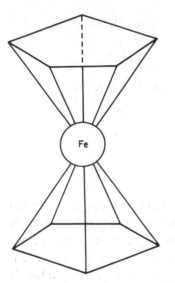

TESTING THEORIES BY SYNTHESIS

There are innumerable examples of compounds which were prepared for the first time in order to test the validity of a theory. In 1893 Alfred Werner proposed his now-famous coordination theory in order to explain the properties of inorganic "complex compounds."[5] At the time of its proposal it was a revolutionary doctrine, and for many years it met with criticism. Although some of the criticisms were not well founded, others were thoroughly sound and challenged Werner's ingenuity and experimental skill to the utmost. For example, the theory predicted optical isomerism for certain types of hexa-coordinate complexes, and Werner succeeded in resolving the cis form of the Co en$_2$(NH$_3$)Br^{2+} ion into d and l forms.[6] But his unyielding critics argued that the optical activity centered in the carbon atoms of the ethylenediamine molecules (even though they are optically inactive themselves). Werner[7] provided final proof that the optical activity of such com-

[4] G. E. Coates, "Organo-Metallic Compounds," John Wiley and Sons, New York, 1956.
[5] A. Werner, Z. anorg. Chem., 3, 267 (1893).
[6] A. Werner, Ber., 44, 1887 (1911).   [7] A. Werner, ibid., 47, 3087 (1914).

pounds lay in the geometrical configuration about the metal ion by effecting the resolution of the tetranuclear complex ion:

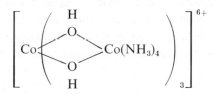

DISCOVERY TO FULFILL A NEED

New compounds are often prepared because of an urgent need for them.

From 1941 to 1945 a great deal of effort was expended in an attempt to find a volatile uranium compound which could be used in the separation of the natural uranium isotopes either by gaseous diffusion, centrifugation, thermal diffusion, or distillation. (Uranium hexafluoride was a known compound at the time and was eventually used, but it was feared that it might prove too difficult to prepare and handle on a large scale.)

The search for new volatile compounds of uranium began with a study of uranium(IV) and (VI) complexes derived from 1,3-diketones and related chelating agents.[8,9] However, it soon became evident that a vapor tension of 0.1 mm at a temperature of 130° could probably not be exceeded and the work was discontinued.

The fact that the hydroborates of aluminum and of beryllium had proved to be the most volatile compounds of these elements suggested the attempt to prepare a hydroborate of uranium. Uranium(IV) hydroborate, $U(BH_4)_4$, as well as the methyl derivatives, $U(BH_4)_3(BH_3CH_3)$ and $U(BH_3CH_3)_4$, were prepared and proved to be the most volatile uranium compounds other than the hexafluoride.[10,11] But of more interest than the preparation of these compounds were the results of efforts to improve the methods of preparing the starting materials and the intermediates required for the preparations. Many new types of reactions were observed, hitherto unknown compounds were discovered, and the chemistry of the boron hydrides was greatly enlarged.[12]

[8] H. I. Schlesinger, H. C. Brown, J. J. Katz, S. Archer, and R. A. Lad, *J. Am. Chem. Soc.*, **75**, 2446 (1953).

[9] H. Gilman, R. G. Jones, E. Bindschadler, D. Blume, G. A. Martin, Jr., J. F. Nobis, J. R. Thirtle, H. L. Yale, and F. A. Yoeman, *ibid.*, **78**, 2790 (1956).

[10] H. I. Schlesinger and H. C. Brown, *ibid.*, **75**, 219 (1953).

[11] H. I. Schlesinger, H. C. Brown, L. Horvitz, A. C. Bond, L. D. Tuck, and A. O. Walker, *ibid.*, **75**, 222 (1953).

[12] H. I. Schlesinger and H. C. Brown, *ibid.*, **75**, 186 (1953).

Another problem which arose during the Atomic Bomb Project was the handling of the very reactive molten metals uranium and plutonium. In a search for new refractories which could be easily formed and sintered into crucibles, yet would be stable and refractory, it was felt that certain sulfides might be useful. Preliminary thermodynamic calculations and estimations indicated that the most stable sulfides should lie in the periodic table around thorium and the rare earth metals. Accordingly the sulfides of the most abundant rare earth, cerium, were investigated.[13] The theretofore unknown CeS was found to be a particularly good refractory which is useful whenever one wishes to avoid contamination of very electropositive metals by oxygen.

New Methods for Preparing Old Compounds

The synthetic chemist is not only concerned with the preparation of new *compounds*—he often seeks new and better *methods* for preparing compounds which have been known for many years. Usually the first method used for the preparation of a compound is inefficient or inconvenient. Thus the motive for seeking a better synthetic procedure (in contrast to the motive for preparing a new compound) is obvious. There are many inorganic compounds which would change from "laboratory curiosities" to commercially important chemicals if practical syntheses were found for them. The compounds B_2Cl_4 and N_4S_4, for example, challenge chemists' ingenuities. In this chapter we shall briefly examine, from a synthetic point of view, the histories of two compounds from the times of their discovery to the present.

BORAZINE

In 1926, Stock and Pohland[14] discovered that when the diammoniate of diborane ($B_2H_6 \cdot 2\ NH_3$) is heated to about 200°, a volatile liquid of composition $B_3N_3H_6$ is formed in yields of about 30 per cent:

$$3\ B_2H_6 \cdot 2\ NH_3 \longrightarrow 2\ B_3N_3H_6 + 12\ H_2 \tag{3}$$

They correctly assumed that the $B_3N_3H_6$ molecule is a ring of alternating BH and NH groups. (See Table 1.1.) This compound, now called borazine, was particularly fascinating because of its structural similarity to benzene. But at the time it was truly a laboratory curiosity because its synthesis required the preparation of diborane, B_2H_6, as an intermediate. Diborane itself was

---

[13] E. D. Eastman, L. Brewer, L. A. Bromley, P. W. Gilles, and N. L. Lofgren, *ibid.*, **72**, 2248 (1950).

[14] A. Stock and E. Pohland, *Ber.*, **59B**, 2215 (1926).

a laboratory curiosity because it was made only by the careful thermal decomposition of tetraborane, B_4H_{10}.

In 1930, Stock, Wiberg, and Martini[15] reported a synthetic method which was better because it did not require the preparation of diborane and because yields of 40 per cent were obtained. The method involved heating the tetrammoniate of tetraborane to 180°:

$$3\ B_4H_{10}{\cdot}4\ NH_3 \longrightarrow 4\ B_3N_3H_6 + 21\ H_2 \tag{4}$$

During the next 20 years, the alkali metal hydroborates were prepared and characterized. These offered a new route to borazine. In 1951, Schaeffer, Schaeffer, and Schlesinger[16] reported that borazine can be obtained in 30–35 per cent yield by heating a mixture of lithium hydroborate and ammonium chloride to 230–300°:

$$3\ LiBH_4 + 3\ NH_4Cl \longrightarrow B_3N_3H_6 + 9\ H_2 + 3\ LiCl \tag{5}$$

More recently, borazine has been prepared by the reduction of B-trichloroborazine. The methods for the preparation of B-trichloroborazine and for its subsequent reduction have undergone continual improvement.

In 1949, Laubengayer and Brown[17] reported that B-trichloroborazine may be prepared in 35 per cent yield by the reaction of boron trichloride with ammonium chloride at 130–175°:

$$3\ BCl_3 + 3\ NH_4Cl \longrightarrow B_3N_3H_3Cl_3 + 9\ HCl \tag{6}$$

In 1959, Eméleus and Videla[18] reported that the yield of the latter reaction may be raised to 60 per cent and that temperatures around 100° may be employed if the ammonium chloride is intimately mixed with a cobalt-on-pumice catalyst. In the same year, Leifield and Hohnstedt[19] described the synthesis of B-trichloroborazine by the reaction of an equal-volume mixture of boron trichloride and ammonia at 100°:

$$3\ BCl_3 + 3\ NH_3 \longrightarrow B_3N_3H_3Cl_3 + 6\ HCl \tag{7}$$

Although the solid product contains about 35 per cent ammonium chloride by weight, practically all of the boron trichloride which is consumed is converted to B-trichloroborazine.

[15] A. Stock, F. Wiberg, and H. Martini, *Ber.*, **63**, 2927 (1930).

[16] G. W. Schaeffer, R. Schaeffer, and H. I. Schlesinger, *J. Am. Chem. Soc.*, **73**, 1612 (1951).

[17] A. W. Laubengayer and C. A. Brown, Paper given at the American Chemical Society meeting, September 19, 1949. See *J. Am. Chem. Soc.*, **77**, 3699 (1955).

[18] H. J. Eméleus and G. J. Videla, *J. Chem. Soc.*, 1306 (1959).

[19] R. F. Leifield and L. F. Hohnstedt, Paper given at the American Chemical Society meeting, April 9, 1959.

Schlesinger and his co-workers[20] showed that B-trichloroborazine may be hydrogenolyzed by treatment with an ether solution of lithium hydroborate:

$$3 \text{ LiBH}_4 + \text{B}_3\text{N}_3\text{H}_3\text{Cl}_3 \longrightarrow \text{B}_3\text{N}_3\text{H}_6 + 3/2 \text{ B}_2\text{H}_6 + 3 \text{ LiCl} \qquad (8)$$

This reduction suffers from two disadvantages. First, it is troublesome disposing of the diborane which is formed as a by-product. Second, it is very difficult to separate borazine from ethers, since azeotropes seem to form. These difficulties were removed by Leifield and Hohnstedt,[19] who carried out the reduction with sodium *tris*isopropoxyhydroborate in isopropyl borate as solvent:

$$3 \text{ NaHB(i—OC}_3\text{H}_7)_3 + \text{B}_3\text{N}_3\text{H}_3\text{Cl}_3 \longrightarrow \text{B}_3\text{N}_3\text{H}_6 + 3 \text{ B(i—OC}_3\text{H}_7)_3$$
$$+ 3 \text{ NaCl} \qquad (9)$$

Borazine may be recovered in 20 per cent yield by distillation from the reaction flask.

DIAMIDOPHOSPHORIC ACID

Stokes[21] first prepared diamidophosphoric acid by the scheme outlined below:

$$\text{POCl}_3 \xrightarrow[\Delta]{\text{C}_6\text{H}_5\text{OH}} \text{POCl}_2\text{OC}_6\text{H}_5 \xrightarrow[\text{NH}_3]{\text{aq. or alc.}} \text{PO(NH}_2)_2\text{OC}_6\text{H}_5$$

$$\downarrow \begin{array}{c} \text{aq.} \\ \text{OH}^- \end{array}$$

$$\text{HOPO(NH}_2)_2 \xleftarrow[\text{HOAc}]{\text{cold conc.}} \text{PO}_2(\text{NH}_2)_2^-$$

The scheme involves the phenolysis of one of the chlorines of phosphorus oxytrichloride followed by the ammonolysis of the remaining chlorines. The phenyl diamidophosphate is then saponified and the free acid is precipitated with cold acetic acid. Audrieth and Toy[22] carried out the ammonolysis in liquid ammonia and thus avoided any hydrolysis of the chlorines. The diamidophosphate is but slightly soluble in liquid ammonia, whereas ammonium chloride is quite soluble.

Kirsanov and Abrazhanova[23] reported an interesting, if impractical, method for preparing diamidophosphates. They found that the compound

[20] R. Schaeffer, M. Steindler, L. Hohnstedt, H. S. Smith, Jr., L. B. Eddy, and H. I. Schlesinger, *J. Am. Chem. Soc.*, **76**, 3303 (1954).

[21] H. N. Stokes, *Am. Chem. J.*, **15**, 198 (1893).

[22] L. F. Audrieth and A. D. F. Toy, *J. Am. Chem. Soc.*, **63**, 2117 (1941).

[23] A. V. Kirsanov, *Sbornik Statei Obshchei Khim.*, **2**, 1046 (1953); A. V. Kirsanov and E. A. Abrazhanova, *ibid.*, **2**, 1059 (1953); *cf. Chem. Abstracts*, **49**, 3051, 5406 (1955).

$C_6H_5SO_2N=P(NH_2)_3$ undergoes hydrolysis to give benzene sulfonamide and diamidophosphate.

$$NaC_6H_5SO_2NCl \xrightarrow{PCl_3} C_6H_5SO_2N=PCl_3 \xrightarrow[\text{in } CCl_4]{NH_3} C_6H_5SO_2N=P(NH_2)_3$$

$$C_6H_5SO_2N=P(NH_2)_3 \Big\langle \begin{array}{l} \nearrow^{H_2O}_{\Delta} \; C_6H_5SO_2NH_2 + NH_4^+ + PO_2(NH_2)_2^- \\[2em] \searrow_{\text{aq. OH}^-} \; C_6H_5SO_2NH_2 + PO_2(NH_2)_2^- \end{array}$$

The hydrolysis may involve phosphorus oxytriamide as an intermediate and suggests that the latter might be a useful starting point for the synthesis. Klement and Koch[24] prepared this compound by the reaction of ammonia with phosphorus oxytrichloride in cold chloroform solution and then hydrolyzed it to the diamidophosphate ion:

$$POCl_3 \xrightarrow[\text{in } CHCl_3]{NH_3} PO(NH_2)_3 \xrightarrow{\text{aq. OH}^-} PO_2(NH_2)_2^-$$

$$\Big\downarrow \text{HOAc}$$

$$HOPO(NH_2)_2$$

Only a rather impure acid is obtained by acidification of the alkaline solutions of diamidophosphate which are involved in the above procedures. Becke-Goehring and Sambeth[25] avoided the alkaline-solution step by hydrogenation of phenyl diamidophosphate directly to the free acid and cyclohexane.

$$C_6H_5OPO(NH_2)_2 + 4 H_2 \xrightarrow[\text{catalyst}]{\text{Adams'}} HOPO(NH_2)_2 + C_6H_{12} \quad (10)$$

[24] R. Klement and O. Koch, *Ber.*, **87**, 333 (1954).
[25] M. Becke-Goehring and J. Sambeth, *Ber.*, **90**, 2075 (1957).

CHAPTER 2

PRELIMINARIES
TO SYNTHESIS

SEARCHING THE LITERATURE

Before carrying out any synthetic work, you should survey the literature. The thoroughness of the literature survey depends upon the scope of the work. If you plan to embark on a systematic study of a class of compounds, to explore a new field of chemistry, or to develop a new method for preparing a compound, the literature survey should be extremely thorough. On the other hand, if you plan to prepare a compound which is fairly well characterized, the literature survey may be cursory—amounting to an hour or two in the library. We shall discuss the general procedure for making a cursory survey of this type.

If you are not familiar with one of the elements in the compound to be synthesized, your first step should be to read about the chemistry of that element in some reference book such as one of those in Table 2.1.

This reading should provide you with enough background so that you can understand other literature regarding the element and so that you can make modifications or improvements of synthetic methods which you will find in the literature.

Your next step should be to seek several synthetic methods, or "recipes," for the compound in question. There are several places in which you may search.

TABLE 2.1

General Reference Books on Inorganic Chemistry

H. J. Eméleus and J. S. Anderson, "Modern Aspects of Inorganic Chemistry," 3rd ed., Van Nostrand, New York, 1960.

W. Hückel (L. H. Long, trans.), "Structural Chemistry of Inorganic Compounds," vols. I and II, Elsevier, New York, 1950.

J. Kleinberg, W. J. Argersinger, Jr. and E. Griswold, "Inorganic Chemistry," Heath and Co., Boston, 1960.

W. M. Latimer, "Oxidation Potentials," 2nd ed., Prentice-Hall, Englewood Cliffs, N. J., 1952.

W. M. Latimer and J. H. Hildebrand, "Reference Book of Inorganic Chemistry," 3rd ed., Macmillan, New York, 1951.

T. Moeller, "Inorganic Chemistry," John Wiley and Sons, New York, 1952.

H. Rémy (J. S. Anderson, trans.), "Treatise on Inorganic Chemistry," vols. I and II, Elsevier, New York, 1956.

Sidgwick, "Chemical Elements and Their Compounds," vols. I and II, Clarendon Press, Oxford, 1950.

M. C. Sneed, J. L. Maynard, and R. C. Brasted, "Comprehensive Inorganic Chemistry," Van Nostrand, New York, 1953.

1. THE SUBJECT OR FORMULA INDEX IN THE MOST RECENT VOLUME OF "INORGANIC SYNTHESES" (MCGRAW-HILL BOOK CO.). These indexes are cumulative, so there is no need to look in the index of any but the most recent volume.

2. GMELIN, "HANDBUCH DER ANORGANISCHEN CHEMIE" or PASCAL, "NOUVEAU TRAITÉ DE CHIMIE MINÉRALE." You will seldom find any detailed recipes in these treatises, but you will find literature references to synthetic methods. These references were not listed in Table 2.1 because they are too encyclopedic for a preliminary, general study of an element. However, they are unexcelled as comprehensive treatises and are very useful when making literature surveys.

3. THE SUBJECT AND FORMULA INDEXES TO CHEMICAL ABSTRACTS. It should be noticed that there are both annual indexes and decennial indexes. There is no need to search in the annual index for any year covered by a decennial index. The abstracts in *Chemical Abstracts* seldom include detailed

synthetic procedures. However, they will help you to decide whether it will be profitable to look up the original articles.

4. VARIOUS TEXTS ON INORGANIC PREPARATIONS, such as those listed in Table 2.2. The book by Brauer is the most valuable of all those listed.

TABLE 2.2

Texts on Synthetic Inorganic Chemistry

G. Brauer, "Handbuch der Präparativen Anorganischen Chemie," Ferdinand Enke, Stuttgart, 1954.

G. E. Coates, "Organo-Metallic Compounds," John Wiley and Sons, New York, 1956.

R. E. Dodd and P. L. Robinson, "Experimental Inorganic Chemistry," Elsevier, New York, 1954.

W. E. Henderson and W. C. Fernelius, "A Course in Inorganic Preparations," McGraw-Hill, New York, 1935.

A. King and A. J. E. Welch, "Inorganic Preparations, A Systematic Course of Experiments," 2nd ed., George Allen and Unwin, London, 1950.

H. Lux, "Anorganisch-Chemische Experimentierkunst," 2nd ed., Johann A. Barth Verlag, Leipzig, 1959.

W. G. Palmer, "Experimental Inorganic Chemistry," Cambridge University Press, 1954.

H. Rheinboldt and O. Schmitz-DuMont, "Chemische Unterrichtsversuche," Theodor Steinkopff, Dresden, 1953.

H. F. Walton, "Inorganic Preparations," Prentice-Hall, Englewood Cliffs, N. J., 1948.

5. If all the above methods fail, it is likely that the compound was discovered only in the last two or three years. If you know the journal in which it is likely that articles on the compound have appeared, it is sometimes fruitful to look through the RECENT ANNUAL INDEXES of that journal. Most articles on inorganic chemistry appear in the following journals:

> Journal of the American Chemical Society
> Zeitschrift für anorganische und allgemeine Chemie
> Journal of Inorganic and Nuclear Chemistry
> Journal of the Chemical Society (London)
> Zhurnal neorganicheskoi Khimii (English translation by Infosearch. Ltd. for the Chemical Society of London)

6. You may be lucky enough to know SOMEBODY WHO IS WORKING WITH COMPOUNDS LIKE THE ONE IN WHICH YOU ARE INTERESTED. Ask him about the compound; he may be able to save you a great deal of time.

Two of the texts listed in Table 2.2 (those by Dodd and Robinson and by Lux) are primarily books on experimental techniques. However, as a source of experimental techniques, the series of volumes entitled "Technique of Organic Chemistry" (Arnold Weissberger, editor; Interscience Publishers, New York) is almost as valuable to the inorganic chemist as to the organic chemist. Some of the volumes and the pertinent topics are listed below:

Vol. I, Part I (2nd ed., 1949).

E. L. Skau and H. Wakeham, "Determination of Melting and Freezing Temperatures," p. 49.

W. Swietoslawski and J. R. Anderson, "Determination of Boiling and Condensation Temperatures," p. 107.

G. W. Thomson, "Determination of Vapor Pressure," p. 141.

Vol. III (1950).

R. S. Egly, "Heating and Cooling," p. 1.

H. B. Golding, "Centrifuging," p. 143.

R. S. Tipson, "Crystallization and Recrystallization," p. 363.

A. B. Cummins, "Filtration," p. 485.

G. Broughton, "Solvent Removal, Evaporation and Drying," p. 605.

Vol. III, Part I (2nd ed., 1956)

L. C. and D. Craig, "Laboratory Extraction and Countercurrent Distribution," p. 149.

Vol. IV (1951).

A. Weissberger *et al.*, "Distillation."

Vol. VII (2nd ed., 1955).

A. Weissberger, E. Proskauer, J. Riddick, and E. Toops, Jr., "Organic Solvents." (Physical properties and methods of purification.)

THERMODYNAMIC CONSIDERATIONS

A good working knowledge of thermodynamics is invaluable to a synthetic chemist. It is unfortunate for arguments for this viewpoint that many brilliant synthetic chemists have very poor backgrounds in chemical thermodynamics. It is therefore a common opinion that thermodynamics is of little value in preparative work. This opinion is further fostered by the unfortunate efforts of chemists who know a little thermodynamics, but who apply it incorrectly.

A discussion of the fundamental principles of thermodynamics is beyond the scope of this book. Therefore we shall assume that the student has learned these principles elsewhere and shall discuss only the applications (and not the derivations) of thermodynamic relations.

Of all the thermodynamic functions, free energy is the most important to chemists. The net change in free energy for a reaction is a measure of the driving force for the reaction. It is related to other thermodynamic quantities by the following equations:

$$\Delta F = -RT \ln K/Q = \Delta H - T\Delta S = -nE\mathscr{F} \qquad (2.1)$$

where $\Delta F \equiv$ change in free energy;

$Q \equiv$ reaction quotient, or the product of the activities of the resulting substances divided by the product of the activities of the reacting substances, each activity raised to a power equal to the coefficient of the substance in the chemical equation;

$K \equiv$ equilibrium constant, or the value of Q at equilibrium;

$\Delta H \equiv$ change in heat content;

$\Delta S \equiv$ change in entropy;

$E \equiv$ potential of the reaction;

$n \equiv$ number of Faradays of electricity involved in the reaction.

Following are the usual units employed and the corresponding values of the constants: ΔF and ΔH, calorie mole^{-1}; ΔS, calorie mole^{-1} degree^{-1}; E, volts. $R = 1.987$ calorie mole^{-1} degree^{-1}; $\mathscr{F} = 23{,}060$ calorie volt^{-1} equivalent^{-1}. At $298.15°$, $RT \ln K/Q = 1364 \log K/Q$.

When $Q = 1$ (which is the case when all the reactants and products are at unit activity), the thermodynamic functions possess their "standard" values:

$$\Delta F° = -RT \ln K = \Delta H° - T\Delta S° = -nE°\mathscr{F} \qquad (2.2)$$

Equilibrium constants are known, or calculable, for many thousands of reactions. It would be impractical to tabulate all of these. It has been found more practical to tabulate free energies, heats, and entropies for *individual species* (rather than for reactions) and to tabulate potentials for *half-reactions*.[1] The utility of such tables in synthetic chemistry will be demonstrated in several examples.

Consider the case of a chemist who wishes to know whether or not he

[1] Both types of functions are tabulated in W. M. Latimer, "Oxidation Potentials," 2nd ed., Prentice-Hall, Englewood Cliffs, N. J., 1952.

can make hydrazine by the oxidation of aqueous ammonia by nitric oxide. From a table of *free energies of formation*, he could obtain the following data:

Species	ΔF_f° (25°), *kcal./mole*
H_2O (*l*)	-56.69
N_2H_4 (aq)	30.56
NO (g)	20.72
NH_3 (aq)	-6.36

Thus he could calculate $\Delta F^\circ = +48.86$ kcal./mole and $K = 1.5 \times 10^{-36}$ for the reaction,

$$8\ NH_3 + 2\ NO_{(g)} = 5\ N_2H_4 + 2\ H_2O \qquad (2.3)$$

He would then know that, under ordinary conditions, the reaction cannot proceed sufficiently to give an appreciable concentration of hydrazine.

TABLE 2.3

Some Aqueous Couples Used in Synthetic Chemistry[1]

ACID SOLUTIONS

Couple	E°
$Mg = Mg^{2+} + 2e^-$	2.37
$Al = Al^{3+} + 3e^-$	1.66
$Zn = Zn^{2+} + 2e^-$	0.76
$H_3PO_2 + H_2O = H_3PO_3 + 2\ H^+ + 2e^-$	0.50
$BH_4^- + 3\ H_2O = H_3BO_3 + 7\ H^+ + 8e^-$	0.47
$Sn = Sn^{2+} + 2e^-$	0.14
$HS_2O_4^- + 2\ H_2O = 2\ H_2SO_3 + H^+ + 2e^-$	0.08
$H_{2(g)} = 2\ H^+ + 2e^-$	0.00
$HCHO + H_2O = HCOOH + 2\ H^+ + 2e^-$	-0.06
$H_2S = S + 2\ H^+ + 2e^-$	-0.14
$Sn^{2+} = Sn^{4+} + 2e^-$	-0.15
$H_2SO_3 + H_2O = SO_4^{2-} + 4\ H^+ + 2e^-$	-0.17
$Fe(CN)_6^{4-} = Fe(CN)_6^{3-} + e^-$	-0.36
$3\ I^- = I_3^- + 2e^-$	-0.54
$HAsO_2 + 2\ H_2O = H_3AsO_4 + 2\ H^+ + 2e^-$	-0.56
$H_2O_2 = O_{2(g)} + 2\ H^+ + 2e^-$	-0.68
$NO_{(g)} + 2\ H_2O = NO_3^- + 4\ H^+ + 4e^-$	-0.96
$2\ Br^- = Br_2 + 2e^-$	-1.06
$2\ H_2O = O_{2(g)} + 4\ H^+ + 4e^-$	-1.23
$2\ Cr^{3+} + 7\ H_2O = Cr_2O_7^{2-} + 14\ H^+ + 6e^-$	-1.33
$2\ Cl^- = Cl_{2(g)} + 2e^-$	-1.36

$$Pb^{2+} + 2 H_2O = PbO_2 + 4 H^+ + 2e^- \qquad -1.46$$
$$Mn^{2+} + 4 H_2O = MnO_4^- + 8 H^+ + 5e^- \qquad -1.51$$
$$IO_3^- + 3 H_2O = H_5IO_6 + H^+ + 2e^- \qquad -1.60$$
$$MnO_2 + 2 H_2O = MnO_4^- + 4 H^+ + 3e^- \qquad -1.70$$
$$2 H_2O = H_2O_2 + 2 H^+ + 2e \qquad -1.77$$
$$2 SO_4^{2-} = S_2O_8^{2-} + 2e^- \qquad -2.01$$
$$O_{2(g)} + H_2O = O_{3(g)} + 2 H^+ + 2e^- \qquad -2.07$$

BASIC SOLUTIONS

Couple	$E°$
$Mg + 2 OH^- = Mg(OH)_2 + 2e^-$	2.69
$Al + 4 OH^- = H_2AlO_3^- + H_2O + 3e^-$	2.35
$BH_4^- + 4 OH^- = H_2BO_3^- + 2 H_2 + H_2O + 4e^-$	1.60
$H_2PO_2^- + 3 OH^- = HPO_3^{2-} + 2 H_2O + 2e^-$	1.57
$Zn + 4 OH^- = ZnO_2^{2-} + 2 H_2O + 2e^-$	1.22
$S_2O_4^{2-} + 4 OH^- = 2 SO_3^{2-} + 2 H_2O + 2e^-$	1.12
$SO_3^{2-} + 2 OH^- = SO_4^{2-} + H_2O + 2e^-$	0.93
$Sn + 3 OH^- = HSnO_2^- + H_2O + 2e^-$	0.91
$H_{2(g)} + 2 OH^- = 2 H_2O + 2e^-$	0.83
$AsO_2^- + 4 OH^- = AsO_4^{3-} + 2 H_2O + 2e^-$	0.67
$S^{2-} = S + 2e^-$	0.48
$Cr(OH)_3 + 5 OH^- = CrO_4^{2-} + 4 H_2O + 3e^-$	0.13
$HO_2^- + OH^- = O_{2(g)} + H_2O + 2e^-$	0.08
$PbO + 2 OH^- = PbO_2 + H_2O + 2e^-$	-0.25
$4 OH^- = O_{2(g)} + 2 H_2O + 4e^-$	-0.40
$I^- + 2 OH^- = IO^- + H_2O + 2e^-$	-0.49
$MnO_2 + 4 OH^- = MnO_4^- + 2 H_2O + 3e^-$	-0.59
$IO_3^- + 3 OH^- = H_3IO_6^{2-} + 2e^-$	-0.70
$Br^- + 2 OH^- = BrO^- + H_2O + 2e^-$	-0.76
$3 OH^- = HO_2^- + H_2O + 2e^-$	-0.88
$Cl^- + 2 OH^- = ClO^- + H_2O + 2e^-$	-0.89
$O_{2(g)} + 2 OH^- = O_{3(g)} + H_2O + 2e^-$	-1.24
$2 SO_4^{2-} = S_2O_8^{2-} + 2e^-$	-2.01

Suppose we wish to prepare periodate by oxidizing iodate with some aqueous oxidizing agent. In Table 2.3 we see that the iodate-periodate couple has a potential of −1.6 volt in acid solutions and a potential of −0.7 volt in basic solutions. Any oxidizing agent whose potential is more negative than −1.6 volt in acid solutions or −0.7 volt in basic solutions is thermodynamically capable of oxidizing iodate to periodate. In practice, hypobromite or hypochlorite is usually used, because these oxidizing agents react with reasonable rapidity and are relatively cheap. Either of these oxidizing agents may be conveniently prepared by dissolving the appropriate halogen in an alkaline solution:

$$2e^- + Cl_{2(g)} = 2\,Cl^- \qquad\qquad E° = +1.36$$
$$Cl^- + 2\,OH^- = ClO^- + H_2O + 2e^- \qquad E° = -0.89$$

$$Cl_{2(g)} + 2\,OH^- = Cl^- + ClO^- + H_2O \qquad E° = +0.47;$$
$$K = 8 \times 10^{15}$$

Consider a gaseous phase containing several types of molecules which is in equilibrium with a liquid or solid phase. How will the molecular composition of the gas change with increasing temperature? For simplicity, let us first consider a gaseous phase which contains only two species; a monomeric species and a dimeric species, both in equilibrium with the same liquid phase. From equation 2.2 we see that the logarithm of the pressure of the monomer, M, and the dimer, D, may be expressed as follows:

$$\ln P_M = \Delta S_M°/R - \Delta H_M°/RT \qquad (2.4)$$

$$\ln P_D = \Delta S_D°/R - \Delta H_D°/RT. \qquad (2.5)$$

Using these equations, we may write

$$\ln P_M/P_D = (\Delta S_M° - \Delta S_D°)/R - (\Delta H_M° - \Delta H_D°)/RT. \qquad (2.6)$$

Hence, we see that the gaseous species corresponding to the higher heat of reaction (more positive $\Delta H°$) will increase in relative importance as the temperature is raised. In general, $\Delta H_D°$ will be greater than $\Delta H_M°$, so the proportion of dimer will usually increase with increasing temperature. This principle may be extended to other polymeric systems. Therefore, if we seek a gaseous system containing a large variety of molecular species of complex structure, we should go to the highest possible temperature at which the saturated system can still exist. For example: at low temperatures the main gaseous species in equilibrium with solid molybdenum trioxide is Mo_3O_9, but as the temperature is increased the proportions of Mo_4O_{12} and Mo_5O_{15} steadily increase.[2]

KINETIC CONSIDERATIONS

When working with thermodynamic data, it is always important to keep in mind that thermodynamics can only tell us whether or not a reaction is *capable* of taking place; it cannot tell us the reaction rate. Thus, a reaction may be thermodynamically favored ($\Delta F < 0$) and yet proceed extremely slowly. Therefore, both kinetics and thermodynamics must be considered.

At a particular temperature, the rate of a reaction may be expressed as

[2] L. Brewer, *J. Chem. Education*, **35**, 153 (1958).

some function of the concentration of the reactants and products. For example, the rate of decomposition of aqueous nitrous acid,

$$3\ HNO_2 = H^+ + NO_3^- + 2\ NO + H_2O, \tag{2.7}$$

may be expressed by the following rate law:[3]

$$\frac{-d(HNO_2)}{dt} = \frac{k_1(HNO_2)^4}{(NO)^2} - k_2(HNO_2)(H^+)(NO_3^-). \tag{2.8}$$

Some reactions have rate laws which involve species not appearing in the net reaction. Such species are called catalysts. For example: the reduction of aqueous dichromate by molecular hydrogen is catalyzed by silver ion.[4] The data fit the following rate law:

$$\frac{-d(H_2)}{dt} = k_1(Ag^+)^2(H_2) + \frac{k_2(Ag^+)^2(H_2)}{k_3(H^+) + (Ag^+)}. \tag{2.9}$$

The decomposition of arsine to arsenic and hydrogen is catalyzed by arsenic surfaces.[5] The rate law is

$$\frac{d(H_2)}{dt} = kSP_{AsH_3} \tag{2.10}$$

where S is the surface area of arsenic and P_{AsH_3} is the pressure of arsine.

Uncatalyzed heterogeneous reactions are characterized by the presence of reactants or products in more than one phase. Oftentimes the rates of such reactions are not only affected by the concentrations of the reactants, but also by conditions which influence the overall rate of transfer of the reactants to the interface between the phases. Such reactions are "diffusion-influenced" and may be accelerated by stirring and by increasing the interfacial area. The reaction of sodium with a solution of chlorobenzene in toluene and the reaction of gaseous arsine with a solution of sodium in ammonia are examples of diffusion-influenced reactions. The rate laws for such reactions are usually quite complicated and are discussed in various chemical engineering texts.[6]

The k's which appear in equations 2.8–2.10 are called *rate constants*. Any rate constant may be expressed in terms of the absolute temperature, an entropy of activation, $\Delta S^\ddagger$, and a heat of activation, $\Delta H^\ddagger$:

$$k_r = \frac{kT}{h} e^{\Delta S^\ddagger/R} e^{-\Delta H^\ddagger/RT} \tag{2.11}$$

[3] D. M. Yost and H. Russell, Jr., "Systematic Inorganic Chemistry," Prentice-Hall, Englewood Cliffs, N. J., 1946.

[4] A. H. Webster and J. Halpern, *J. Phys. Chem.*, **61**, 1239 (1957).

[5] K. Tamaru, *J. Phys. Chem.*, **59**, 777 (1955).

[6] See, for example, O. A. Hougen and K. M. Watson, "Chemical Process Principles. Part 3. Kinetics and Catalysis," John Wiley and Sons, New York, 1947.

(here k_r is the rate constant, k is the Boltzmann constant, and h is Planck's constant.) Every reaction path has its characteristic values of $\Delta S^\ddagger$ and $\Delta H^\ddagger$. It can be seen that the exponential term involving the heat of activation is very important in determining the effect of temperature on the rate constant. For example, with a heat of activation of 11 kcal./mole, a rate constant will approximately double for each 10° rise in temperature near room temperature.

We see that there are two general methods for regulating reaction rates. The concentrations of the species which occur in the rate law may be changed; and the temperature may be changed. Heterogeneous reactions may be speeded up by increasing the surface area at which reaction takes place. If a rate is diffusion-influenced, stirring will increase the rate.

In the case of an exothermic reaction ($\Delta H^\circ < 0$), care must be taken that the temperature is not raised too far in order to increase the rate. As a rough approximation, we may consider ΔH° and ΔS° to be independent of temperature. From equation 2.2 we see that

$$\ln K = \Delta S^\circ / R - \Delta H^\circ / RT. \tag{2.12}$$

If the temperature is increased sufficiently, the equilibrium constant is principally determined by the entropy of the reaction. If ΔS° is negative, the equilibrium constant will be less than one and any advantage gained by increasing the rate may be offset by reversing the equilibrium.

Several examples of the use of kinetic reasoning in syntheses are given below.

The Haber process for the industrial synthesis of ammonia involves both equilibrium and kinetic considerations. Hydrogen and nitrogen react at high temperatures and pressures and in the presence of an iron catalyst according to the reversible reaction

$$N_{2(g)} + 3\,H_{2(g)} = 2\,NH_{3(g)}. \tag{2.13}$$

The effect of temperature and pressure on the equilibrium is given in Table 2.4. The formation of ammonia is obviously favored by both low temperatures and high pressures, but if the temperature falls much below 400°, the rate of the catalyzed reaction is too slow for economical production. On the other hand, if the temperature is too high, the equilibrium pressure of ammonia is too low for satisfactory yields. In practice, pressures around 1000 atmospheres and temperatures around 500° are employed.

There are many compounds which are thermodynamically stable at low temperatures but which disproportionate at higher temperatures. In certain cases these compounds are stable only at temperatures where the rate of formation is slow. As a consequence, these compounds are often difficult to produce and probably many of them remain undiscovered. However,

CHAPTER 3

ACID-BASE
CONCEPTS

A synthetic chemist is judged by his ability to choose reagents and conditions for the preparation of compounds. This ability goes hand in hand with the ability to predict the products of a reaction when only the reactants and conditions are known. Chemists who are successful at such predictions are usually quite adept at choosing chemical analogues. In analogy, one infers that two or more things are similar in some respect because they are similar in some other respect. In a chemical analogy, one reasons that two different compounds will react similarly under certain circumstances (or may be synthesized by similar reactions) because, on the basis of some other scheme of classification, they are similar. Without a scheme of classification, there is no basis for analogy. Thus, one of the important jobs of chemists is to devise and evaluate schemes for classifying compounds and reactions. Classification on the basis of acid-base properties has been found to be particularly useful. In this chapter we shall first briefly examine the development of acid-base concepts and then observe how certain concepts have proved useful in particular syntheses.

PROTONIC ACID-BASE CONCEPTS

On the basis of the Arrhenius theory of electrolytic dissociation, an acid is a hydrogen-containing compound which yields hydrogen ions in water solution and a base is a hydroxyl compound which yields hydroxide ions in water solution. The process of neutralization is then the combination of hydrogen ions and hydroxide ions to form water. This simple concept is very useful and should be used whenever it is adequate.

However, Brönsted[1] felt that a more general acid-base concept was needed in order that reactions of the following types could be classified as acid-base reactions:

$$R_3N: + HOAc = R_3NH^+ + OAc^- \qquad (3.1)$$

$$CO_3^{2-} + H_2O = HCO_3^- + OH^-. \qquad (3.2)$$

In his concept, acids and bases are related by the following "half-reaction":

$$acid = base + H^+. \qquad (3.3)$$

That is, an acid is a hydrogen-containing species capable of acting as a proton donor, and a base is a species capable of acting as a proton acceptor. Thus, acids and bases are independent of a solvent and bear no relationship to salts. Under this concept, acid-base equilibria are competitions among bases for protons. A typical acid-base reaction may then be written

$$acid_1 + base_2 = acid_2 + base_1. \qquad (3.4)$$

In this reaction, *acid₁* is the *conjugate acid* of *base₁* and *base₁* is the *conjugate base* of *acid₁*. That is, by adding a proton to *base₁*, we obtain *acid₁*. The same formal relationships exist between *acid₂* and *base₂*. It will be noted that reactions 3.1 and 3.2 fall into this scheme. The Arrhenius concept is embraced by the Brönsted concept as long as we realize that the aqueous proton is hydrated. The oxonium ion, H_3O^+, is one of the cationic species in an aqueous solution of a strong acid, and we may write

$$H_3O^+ + OH^- = H_2O + H_2O. \qquad (3.5)$$

Here water may be thought of as either the conjugate acid of the hydroxide ion or as the conjugate base of the oxonium ion.

For many years it has been recognized that certain solvents resemble water in that they undergo self-ionization to give a solvated proton and an anion, and dissolve salts to give conducting solutions. In these solvents, the protonic concept is quite applicable. For example, the solvent liquid ammonia undergoes self-ionization as follows:

$$2\,NH_3 = NH_4^+ + NH_2^- \quad K_{-33°} \approx 10^{-30}. \qquad (3.6)$$

If we look upon the ammonium ion as the acidic species and the amide ion as the basic species, we may define an acid as any species which, when dissolved in ammonia, increases the concentration of ammonium ion and a

[1] J. N. Brönsted, *Rec. trav. chim.*, **42**, 718 (1923).

base as any species which increases the concentration of amide ion. Thus, we may establish a set of *ammono* acids and bases analogous to corresponding *aquo* acids and bases. (See Table 3.1.)

TABLE 3.1

Some *Ammono* and *Aquo* Compounds

Ammono Cpd.	Aquo Cpd.	Cpd. Type
NH_3	H_2O	Solvent
KNH_2	KOH	Base
NH_4Cl	HCl	Protonic acid
CH_3CONH_2	CH_3COOH	"Solvo-acid"
Li_2NH	Li_2O	Ansolvous base
NH_2NO_2	HNO_3	"Solvo-acid"

Anhydrous sulfuric acid self-ionizes in two ways[2]: by "ionic dehydration":

$$2\,H_2SO_4 = H_3O^+ + HS_2O_7^-$$
$$K_{id} = 4.0 \times 10^{-5}\,\text{mole}^2\,\text{kg.}^{-2} \quad (3.7)$$

and by "autoprotolysis."

$$H_2SO_4 = H^+ + HSO_4^-$$
or
$$2\,H_2SO_4 = H_3SO_4^+ + HSO_4^-$$
$$K_{ap} = 2.4 \times 10^{-4}\,\text{mole}^2\,\text{kg.}^{-2} \quad (3.8)$$

If we consider the solvated proton to be the acidic species in sulfuric acid, then the bisulfate ion, HSO_4^-, is the basic species. When water is dissolved in sulfuric acid, the following solvolysis takes place:

$$H_2O + H_2SO_4 = H_3O^+ + HSO_4^-$$
$$K = 1\,\text{mole kg.}^{-1} \quad (3.9)$$

Hence, water is a fairly strong base in sulfuric acid. On the other hand, when sulfur trioxide is dissolved in sulfuric acid, the following solvolysis takes place:

$$SO_3 + H_2SO_4 = H^+ + HS_2O_7^-$$
or
$$H_2S_2O_7 = H^+ + HS_2O_7^-$$
$$K = 0.014\,\text{mole kg.}^{-1} \quad (3.10)$$

Hence, sulfur trioxide is an acid in sulfuric acid. The freezing-point diagram for sulfuric acid solutions of water and of SO_3 is given in Figure 3.1. The marked difference in the slopes of the two arms of the curve reflects the difference in the equilibrium constants for the solvolysis of water and the

[2] R. J. Gillespie and E. A. Robinson, *Advances in Inorganic Chemistry and Radiochemistry*, **1**, 385 (1959).

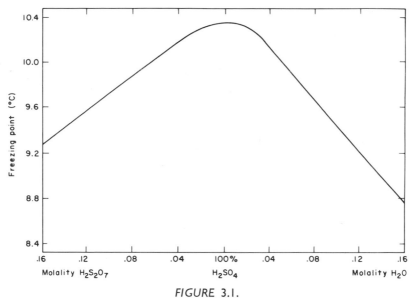

FIGURE 3.1.

Freezing points of solutions of sulfur trioxide and water in sulfuric acid.

ionization of pyrosulfuric acid. Freezing-point depression studies have been very useful in elucidating the nature of many sulfuric acid solutions. For example, such studies have shown that nitric acid reacts in sulfuric acid to give four moles of species. This result may be explained by reaction 3.11:

$$HONO_2 + 2\ H_2SO_4 = NO_2^+ + H_3O^+ + 2\ HSO_4^-. \tag{3.11}$$

It is believed that ethers, alcohols, and carboxylic acids react as follows:

$$R_2O + H_2SO_4 = R_2OH^+ + HSO_4^- \tag{3.12}$$

$$ROH + 2\ H_2SO_4 = ROSO_3H + H_3O^+ + HSO_4^- \tag{3.13}$$

$$RCOOH + 2\ H_2SO_4 = RCO^+ + H_3O^+ + 2\ HSO_4^-. \tag{3.14}$$

Anhydrous hydrogen fluoride self-ionizes to the solvated proton and the bifluoride ion

$$2\ HF = H^+ + HF_2^-. \tag{3.15}$$

Hence, phosphorus pentafluoride is an acid in HF:

$$PF_5 + HF - H^+ + PF_6^- \tag{3.16}$$

and water, nitric acid, and potassium nitrate are bases in HF:

$$H_2O + 2\ HF = H_3O^+ + HF_2^- \tag{3.17}$$

$$HNO_3 + 2\ HF = H_2NO_3^+ + HF_2^- \tag{3.18}$$

$$KNO_3 + 4\ HF = H_2NO_3^+ + K^+ + 2\ HF_2^-. \tag{3.19}$$

APROTIC ACID-BASE CONCEPTS

The "solvent" concept. There are some solvents which undergo self-ionization, whose salt solutions are electrically conducting, and yet which contain no hydrogen. Obviously, the protonic concept cannot be used to identify acid-base reactions in such solvents. In such solvents the usual procedure is to consider the cation formed in the self-ionization as the acidic species and to consider the anion formed in the self-ionization as the basic species. This procedure is the basis of the *"solvent" concept of acids and bases.*

Pure bromine trifluoride is a liquid with a rather high electrical conductivity ($\kappa = 8.1 \times 10^{-3}$ ohm^{-1} cm^{-1} at 15°).[3] The conductivity is explained by assuming the following self-ionization:

$$2\,BrF_3 = BrF_2^+ + BrF_4^-. \tag{3.20}$$

The d.c. electrolysis of bromine trifluoride involves the formation of BrF at the cathode and the formation of BrF_5 at the anode.

$$2\,e^- + BrF_3 + BrF_2^+ = BrF_4^- + BrF \tag{3.21}$$

$$BrF_3 + BrF_4^- = BrF_2^+ + BrF_5 + 2\,e^-. \tag{3.22}$$

At the boundary between the anode and cathode compartments, the recombination reaction occurs:

$$BrF + BrF_5 = 2\,BrF_3. \tag{3.23}$$

The conductivity is achieved by a countercurrent migration of the BrF_2^+ and BrF_4^- ions.

Bromine trifluoride forms adducts with many metal fluorides. Potassium fluoride reacts with BrF_3 to form potassium tetrafluorobromate, $KBrF_4$. Antimony pentafluoride reacts to form difluorobromine(III) hexafluoroantimonate(V), BrF_2SbF_6. According to the "solvent" concept, $KBrF_4$ is a base and BrF_2SbF_6 is an acid in bromine trifluoride. Thus, when solutions of these reagents are mixed, a typical neutralization reaction takes place:

$$BrF_2^+ + BrF_4^- = 2\,BrF_3. \tag{3.24}$$

Liquid sulfur dioxide dissolves many substances to form conducting solutions. Certain rapid reactions, such as the reaction between thionyl chloride and cesium sulfite to give cesium chloride, have been interpreted as neutralization reactions.[4] It was supposed that thionyl compounds ionize

[3] A. Banks, H. Emeléus, and A. Woolf, *J. Chem. Soc.*, 2861 (1949).
[4] G. Jander, "Die Chemie in Wasserähnlichen Lösungsmitteln," Springer-Verlag, Berlin, 1949.

to give the acidic SO^{2+} ion and that sulfites ionize to give the basic SO_3^{2-} ion. Neutralizations were then presumed to proceed by the reaction

$$SO^{2+} + SO_3^{2-} = 2 SO_2. \tag{3.25}$$

The reverse reaction is a plausible self-ionization reaction for sulfur dioxide. However, experiments with radioactive sulfur have shown that, although sulfur is exchanged rapidly between the solvent and dissolved sulfites, essentially no exchange occurs between thionyl halides and the solvent.[5] Hence, equation 3.25 is an unlikely mechanism for neutralizations. Perhaps some mechanism like the following, involving oxide ion transfer, is operative:

$$SOCl_2 = SOCl^+ + Cl^- \tag{3.26}$$

$$SOCl^+ + SO_3^{2-} \longrightarrow SO_2 + SO_2Cl^- \tag{3.27}$$

$$SO_2Cl^- \longrightarrow SO_2 + Cl^-. \tag{3.28}$$

The Lewis concept. The Lewis electronic theory[6] is the most general of the commonly used acid-base concepts. In a Lewis acid-base reaction, a lone electron pair on one atom is used to form a covalent bond to another atom. The acid is the species which "accepts" the electron pair; the base is the species which "donates" the electron pair. The Lewis concept is completely independent of solvent considerations. Indeed, many Lewis acid-base reactions proceed in the gas phase. In Table 3.2 are several examples of Lewis acid-base reactions.

TABLE 3.2

Some Lewis Acid-Base Reactions

Acid		Base		Product
H^+	+	$:\ddot{F}:^-$	=	HF
$(CH_3)_3B$	+	$:NH_3$	=	$(CH_3)_3\bar{B}:\overset{+}{N}H_3$
BCl_3	+	$R\ddot{O}R$	=	$Cl_3\bar{B}:\overset{+}{O}R_2$
Ag^+	+	$2 :\ddot{I}:^-$	=	$IAgI^-$
$SnCl_4$	+	$2 :\ddot{C}l:^-$	=	$SnCl_6^{2-}$
NO_2^+	+	$:\ddot{C}l:^-$	=	NO_2Cl

SOLVATION AND SOLVOLYSIS

The words *solvation* and *solvolysis* are extremely ambiguous. There are probably as many definitions of these words as there are chemists. However,

[5] R. E. Johnson, T. H. Norris, and J. L. Huston, *J. Am. Chem. Soc.*, **73**, 3052 (1951).

[6] G. N. Lewis, "Valence and the Structure of Atoms and Molecules," The Chemical Catalog Co., New York, 1923; *J. Franklin Inst.*, **226**, 293 (1938).

these words are in common use, and it is important that we know the various types of reactions which have been classed under these very general headings.

Solvation. To most chemists, solvation means the addition of one or more solvent molecules to another species. The solvent molecules may retain their identities (that is, intramolecular solvent bonds are not broken), or a considerable rearrangement of atoms may occur. Thus, all the following reactions may be classed as solvations:

$$CaCl_2 + 6\ NH_3 = Ca(NH_3)_6Cl_2 \qquad (3.29)$$

$$BF_3 + 2\ H_2O = H_3O(F_3BOH) \qquad (3.30)$$

$$B_2H_6 + 2\ NH_3 = [BH_2(NH_3)_2]BH_4. \qquad (3.31)$$

Solvolysis. A solvolysis may be considered a solvation in which the solvent molecule is split into two ions. Either one or both solvent-ions may add to other species. We may thus consider three types of solvolyses. (1) In one type of solvolysis, an acid solution is formed. The hydrolysis of sulfur trioxide is an example of this type.

$$SO_3 + H_2O = HSO_4^- + H^+. \qquad (3.32)$$

The following reactions of the ammonium ion and the ferric ion are usually referred to as hydrolyses,

$$NH_4^+ + H_2O = NH_4OH + H^+ \qquad (3.33)$$

$$Fe^{3+} + H_2O = FeOH^{2+} + H^+ \qquad (3.34)$$

although these are probably better considered as simple ionizations of protonic acids:

$$NH_4^+ = NH_3 + H^+ \qquad (3.35)$$

$$Fe(H_2O)_6^{3+} = Fe(H_2O)_5OH^{2+} + H^+. \qquad (3.36)$$

However, we need not limit ourselves to water, or even to protonic solvents. When antimony pentafluoride is dissolved in bromine trifluoride, essentially complete solvolysis occurs and an acid solution is formed:

$$SbF_5 + BrF_3 = BrF_2^+ + SbF_6^-. \qquad (3.37)$$

Similarly, aluminum chloride undergoes solvolysis to give an acid solution in liquid phosgene:

$$AlCl_3 + COCl_2 = COCl^+ + AlCl_4^-. \qquad (3.38)$$

(2) Another type of solvolysis involves the formation of a basic solution. In the following examples, solvent molecules act as protonic acids:

IN WATER:

$$CaC_2 + 2\ H_2O = Ca^{2+} + 2\ OH^- + C_2H_2. \qquad (3.39)$$

IN ACETIC ACID:

$$KH(\text{phthalate}) + HOAc = H_2(\text{phthalate}) + K^+ + OAc^-. \quad (3.40)$$

IN HYDROGEN FLUORIDE:

$$KNO_3 + 4\ HF = K^+ + H_2NO_3^+ + 2\ HF_2^-. \quad (3.41)$$

(3) In some reactions, both ions of the solvent become attached to another species with the breaking of a bond:

$$O{=}C{=}O + H_2O = O{=}C\begin{array}{c}\diagup OH\\ \diagdown OH\end{array}. \quad (3.42)$$

When two or more fragments form, the process is called solvolytic cleavage:

$$^{2-}O_3P{-}O{-}PO_3{}^{2-} + H_2O = 2\ HPO_4{}^{2-} \quad (3.43)$$

$$B(CH_3)_3 + 3\ H_2O = B(OH)_3 + 3\ CH_4 \quad (3.44)$$

$$Cl_2 + H_2O = HOCl + H^+ + Cl^- \quad (3.45)$$

MECHANISMS OF ACID-BASE REACTIONS

Lewis bases are sometimes called *nucleophilic reagents*. Hence, the following type of reaction is often called a *nucleophilic substitution* reaction or S_N reaction.[7]

$$Y{:} + A{-}X \longrightarrow A{-}Y + X{:} \quad (3.46)$$

Such a substitution reaction may proceed by two possible paths—a *dissociation* (S_N1) mechanism, or a *displacement* (S_N2) mechanism. An S_N1 reaction proceeds in two steps. First a unimolecular dissociation takes place (usually rate-determining),

$$A{-}X \longrightarrow A + X{:} \quad (3.47)$$

followed by a coordination

$$Y{:} + A \longrightarrow A{-}Y. \quad (3.48)$$

An S_N2 reaction involves a transition state in which both X and Y are loosely bound to A. Thus the coordination number of A increases by one in the transition state.

$$Y{:} + A{-}X \longrightarrow [Y\cdots A\cdots X] \longrightarrow Y{-}A + X{:} \quad (3.49)$$

In an S_N1 reaction, the rate of substitution should be independent of the nucleophilic reagent, since the latter is not involved in the initial dissociation.

[7] C. K. Ingold, "Structure and Mechanism in Organic Chemistry," Cornell University Press, Ithaca, N. Y., 1953.

In an S_N2 reaction, however, the rate is dependent on the nucleophilic character of the group Y. A good nucleophilic reagent is one which reacts rapidly;
it is usually, but not always, a strong base.

Consider the substitution of a chloride ion in *cis-* Co en$_2$Cl$_2$$^+$ by various
anions:[8]

$$Y:^- + Co\ en_2Cl_2^+ \longrightarrow Co\ en_2ClY^+ + Cl^-. \tag{3.50}$$

From Figure 3.2 we see that the weakly nucleophilic reagents (SCN$^-$, Br$^-$,
Cl$^-$, NO$_3$$^-$) react at the same rate (the rates were also found to be indepen-

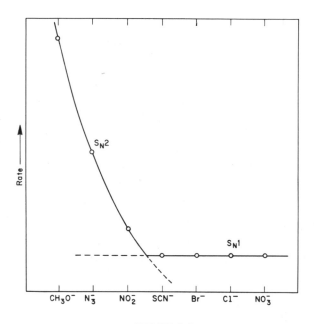

FIGURE 3.2.
Rates of reaction of *cis*-Co(en)$_2$Cl$_2$$^+$ with various anions in methanol.[8]

dent of the concentration of the entering anion); it is presumed that each of
these substitutions is of the S_N1 type. The strongly nucleophilic reagents
(CH$_3$O$^-$, N$_3$$^-$, and NO$_2$$^-$) reacted according to a second-order rate law with
rate constants in the ratio 30,000:100:1, respectively. These substitutions
are presumably of the S_N2 type.

Many "oxidation-reduction" reactions are best thought of as S_N2

[8] D. D. Brown and C. K. Ingold, *J. Chem. Soc.*, 2680 (1953).

substitutions. For example, the oxidation of nitrite by hypochlorous acid is presumed to go by the following mechanism.[9]

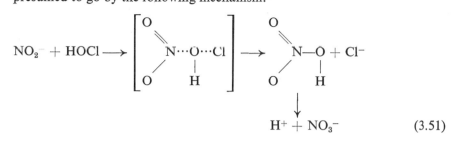

$$H^+ + NO_3^- \qquad (3.51)$$

APPLICATIONS OF ACID-BASE CONCEPTS TO SYNTHESIS

Consider the ten compounds pictured in Figure 3.3. They are all structurally analogous, since they may be thought of as derivatives of carbonic acid in which the —OH groups have been replaced by either —NH_2 or —$NHNH_2$ groups and in which the =O group has been replaced by either =NH or =NNH_2. But what is more important, all of these compounds may be prepared by analogous methods.[10] Just as carbon dioxide, carbonyl chloride (phosgene), and carbon tetrachloride undergo hydrolysis to give carbonic acid, so will the same compounds undergo ammonolysis and hydrazinolysis to give the compounds indicated in Figure 3.3.

$$CO_2 + 2\ NH_3 \longrightarrow NH_4CO_2NH_2 \qquad (3.52)$$
$$\text{(Ammonium salt of carbamic acid)}$$

$$CO_2 + 2\ N_2H_4 \longrightarrow N_2H_5CO_2NHNH_2 \qquad (3.53)$$
$$\text{(Hydrazinium salt of hydrazidocarbonic acid)}$$

$$COCl_2 + 4\ NH_3 \longrightarrow 2\ NH_4Cl + CO(NH_2)_2 \qquad (3.54)$$
$$\text{(Urea)}$$

$$COCl_2 + 4\ N_2H_4 \longrightarrow 2\ N_2H_5Cl + CO(NHNH_2)_2 \qquad (3.55)$$
$$\text{(Carbohydrazide)}$$

$$CCl_4 + 7\ NH_3 \longrightarrow 4\ NH_4Cl + C(NH)(NH_2)_2 \qquad (3.56)$$
$$\text{(Guanidine)}$$

$$CCl_4 + 7\ N_2H_4 \longrightarrow 4\ N_2H_5Cl + C(NNH_2)(NHNH_2)_2 \qquad (3.57)$$
$$\text{(Triaminoguanidine)}$$

The action of hydrazine upon urea results in the displacement of ammonia and the formation of semicarbazide and finally carbohydrazide,

$$H_2NCONH_2 \xrightarrow[-NH_3]{N_2H_4} H_2NCON_2H_3 \xrightarrow[-NH_3]{N_2H_4} H_3N_2CON_2H_3. \qquad (3.58)$$

[9] H. Taube, *Record Chem. Progr. Kresge-Hooker Sci. Lib.*, **17**, 25 (1956).

[10] L. F. Audrieth, "Acids, Bases and Non-Aqueous Systems," Twenty-third Annual Priestley Lectures, University Litho-printers, Ypsilanti, Mich., 1949, pp. 54–5.

FIGURE 3.3

Ammonia and Hydrazine Derivatives of Carbonic Acid[10]

HYDRAZINOLYSIS $\longrightarrow$

$\longleftarrow$———HYDROLYSIS

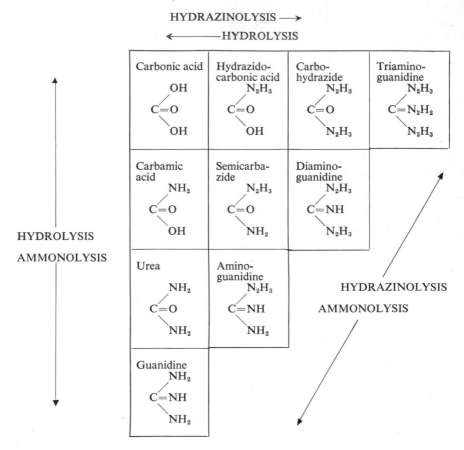

Aminoguanidine may be prepared by the hydrazination of cyanamide (which may be considered an *ammono* carbonic acid).

$$N_2H_5^+ + H_2NCN \longrightarrow C(NH_2)_2N_2H_3^+. \tag{3.59}$$

Diaminoguanidine may be prepared by the hydrazinolysis of cyanogen halides.

$$CNCl + 3 N_2H_4 \longrightarrow CNH(N_2H_3)_2 + N_2H_5Cl. \tag{3.60}$$

The compounds pictured in Figure 3.4 may be very nicely correlated by looking upon them as derivatives of ammonia.[11] Species in brackets are

[11] These compounds are discussed in D. M. Yost and H. Russell, Jr., "Systematic Inorganic Chemistry," Prentice-Hall, Englewood Cliffs, N. J., pp. 98–104 and in W. C. Bray, G. K. Rollefson, R. E. Connick, and R. E. Powell, "Advanced Inorganic Chemistry," p. 35, (Syllabus for Chemistry 120 at the University of California).

unstable and have never been isolated. In general, a compound in the figure may be prepared (1) from the compound below it and to the left by treating the latter with HSO_3^- in neutral aqueous solution; (2) from the compound above it and to the right by hydrolysis in strongly alkaline solution; (3) from the compound to the left by treatment with SO_3; (4) from the compound to the right by hydrolysis in acid solution; and (5) from the compound immediately below by electrolytic reduction.

FIGURE 3.4

Derivatives of Ammonia, Hydroxylamine, and Nitrous Acid

Ammonia NH_3	Amidosulfuric acid $HOSO_2NH_2$	Imidodisulfuric acid $HN(SO_2OH)_2$	Nitridotrisulfuric acid $N(SO_2OH)_3$
Hydroxylamine H_2NOH	Hydroxylamido-sulfuric acid $HONHSO_2OH$	Hydroxylimidodisulfuric acid $HON(SO_2OH)_2$	
Dihydroxylamine $[HN(OII)_2]$ or Nitroxyl $[NOH]$	Dihydroxylamido sulfuric acid $[(HO)_2NSO_2OH]$		
Trihydroxylamine $[N(OH)_3]$ or Nitrous acid $HON=O$			

Most of the protonic solvents are very aggressive in their solvolytic action; consequently, one very seldom observes stepwise solvolysis in these solvents. (Thus it is impossible, under ordinary conditions, to obtain phosphoryl chloride by treating phosphorus pentachloride with water.) On the other hand, liquid sulfur dioxide is very mild in its solvolytic action. Excellent synthetic methods for thionyl chloride, thionyl bromide, niobium oxychloride ($NbOCl_3$), and tungsten oxychloride ($WOCl_4$) are based on the following reactions.[12]

$$PCl_5 + SO_2 \longrightarrow POCl_3 + SOCl_2 \tag{3.61}$$

$$PBr_5 + SO_2 \longrightarrow POBr_3 + SOBr_2 \tag{3.62}$$

[12] G. Jander, "Die Chemie in Wasserähnlichen Lösungsmitteln," Springer-Verlag, Berlin, 1949, pp. 349–50.

$$NbCl_5 + SO_2 \longrightarrow NbOCl_3 + SOCl_2 \tag{3.63}$$

$$WCl_6 + SO_2 \longrightarrow WOCl_4 + SOCl_2 \tag{3.64}$$

The methods for synthesizing the alkali hydroborates and diborane are examples of the use of the Lewis acid-base theory in synthetic chemistry.[13] The following boron compounds are listed in the order of increasing acid strength.

$$B(OCH_3)_3 < B(CH_3)_3 < (BH_3)_2 < BF_3.$$

Each of these compounds will react with an alkali metal hydride to form a borate. For example,

$$NaH + B(OCH_3)_3 \longrightarrow NaBH(OCH_3)_3 \tag{3.65}$$

$$LiH + {}^1/_2 (BH_3)_2 \longrightarrow LiBH_4. \tag{3.66}$$

A stronger acid will displace a weaker one from its adduct. For example,

$$NaBH(OCH_3)_3 + {}^1/_2 (BH_3)_2 \longrightarrow NaBH_4 + B(OCH_3)_3 \tag{3.67}$$

$$3\ NaBH_4 + 4\ BF_3 \xrightarrow{\text{ether}} 3\ NaBF_4 + 2\ (BH_3)_2. \tag{3.68}$$

Reaction 3.68 may be used to prepare diborane, but it requires the reagent sodium hydroborate. The latter compound may be prepared by the disproportionation of sodium trimethoxyhydroborate:

$$4\ NaBH(OCH_3)_3 \xrightarrow{\Delta} NaBH_4 + 3\ NaOCH_3 + 3\ B(OCH_3)_3. \tag{3.69}$$

It has been found that other acids than boron trifluoride may be used to displace diborane from the hydroborate ion. Thus diborane may be conveniently prepared by the addition of sodium hydroborate to concentrated sulfuric acid:

$$NaBH_4 + H_2SO_4 \longrightarrow Na^+ + HSO_4^- + H_2 + {}^1/_2 (BH_3)_2. \tag{3.70}$$

BIBLIOGRAPHY

R. P. Bell, "Acids and Bases. Their Quantitative Behaviour," Methuen and Co., London, 1952.

L. F. Audrieth, "Acids, Bases and Non-Aqueous Systems," Twenty-third Annual Priestley Lectures, University Litho-printers, Ypsilanti, Mich., 1949.

W. F. Luder and S. Zuffanti, "The Electronic Theory of Acids and Bases," John Wiley and Sons, New York, 1946.

L. F. Audrieth and J. Kleinberg, "Non-Aqueous Solvents," John Wiley and Sons, New York, 1953.

[13] H. I. Schlesinger and H. C. Brown, *J. Am. Chem. Soc.*, **75**, 186 (1953).

G. Jander, "Die Chemie in Wasserähnlichen Lösungsmitteln," Springer-Verlag, Berlin, 1949.

F. Basolo and R. G. Pearson, "Mechanisms of Inorganic Reactions," John Wiley and Sons, New York, 1958.

PROBLEMS

1. There are eight conceivable ammonia and hydrazine derivatives of carbonic acid which are not pictured in Figure 3.3 (for example,

$$\text{HO—C—OH}).$$
$$\overset{\|}{\underset{\text{NH}}{}}$$

   Why is it unlikely that any of these are stable compounds?

2. By reference to Figure 3.4, suggest three "routes" from nitrite to hydroxylamine.

3. From the "autoprotolysis" and "ionic dehydration" constants for sulfuric acid (see equations 3.7 and 3.8) calculate the apparent ionization constant.

4. What is the net reaction which takes place when nitryl chloride, NO_2Cl, is formed by bubbling HCl into a solution of nitric acid in sulfuric acid?

5. Six moles of dissolved species are formed when either one mole of boric acid (H_3BO_3) or one mole of boric oxide (B_2O_3) is dissolved in sulfuric acid. Write the net reactions for these dissolution processes.

6. If calcium phosphide (Ca_3P_2) were treated with an alcohol (ROH), which of the following sets of products would you expect? Why?

   a) PR_3 and $Ca(OH)_2$
   b) PH_3 and $Ca(OR)_2$
   c) $P(OR)_3$ and CaH_2
   d) H_3PO_3 and CaR_2.

7. How can you account for the fact that nitryl chloride reacts with water to form hydrochloric acid and nitric acid, whereas nitryl chloride reacts with ammonia to form chloramine (NH_2Cl) and ammonium nitrite?

8. Can you account for the puzzling fact that phosphorus trichloride hydrolyzes to give phosphorous acid and hydrochloric acid, whereas nitrogen trichloride hydrolyzes to give ammonia and hypochlorous acid?

9. Suggest a mechanism for the rapid exchange of $S^*O_3^{2-}$ with SO_2 in liquid SO_2.

CHAPTER 4

SOME SPECIAL TYPES
OF REACTIONS

In this chapter we shall discuss three types of reactions: the reactions of metal coordination compounds, the reactions of metal-ammonia solutions, and the syntheses of hydrides. These types were chosen because they have been reasonably well systematized. The sections on metal coordination compounds and metal-ammonia solutions illustrate the importance of kinetic and mechanistic data to the synthetic chemist. The section on hydrides illustrates that, although many methods may be known for the preparation of compounds of the same class, a particular method is generally useful for only a few of the compounds, and a particular compound may be prepared by only a few of the methods.

Chemistry of Metal Coordination Compounds

THERMODYNAMIC STABILITY OF COMPLEXES

Stable coordination compounds are only formed by metal ions with high charges or small radii. Thus the alkali metal ions have little tendency to form complexes, whereas the transition metal ions form a multitude of complex ions. Metals may be arranged into series which roughly give the order of decreasing complex stability.

For univalent ions,

$$Ag > Tl > Li > Na > K > Rb > Cs.$$

For bivalent ions,

$$Pt > Pd > Hg > UO_2 > Be > Cu > Ni > Co > Pb >$$
$$Zn > Cd > Fe > Mn > Ca > Sr > Ba.$$

For tervalent ions,

$$Co > Cr > Fe > Ga > Al > Sc > In > Y > Pr > Ce > La.$$

There are many exceptions to these lists, so they are not to be taken too seriously.

The order of metal ions in such stability series is influenced by the nature of the coordinated groups (ligands). For example, we may classify metals into two groups, depending on their relative affinities for ligands with oxygen and nitrogen donor atoms.[1] Generally, metal ions with "inert-gas" electronic configurations have a greater affinity for oxygen than for nitrogen, whereas the reverse is true for "non-inert gas" ions such as those of the transition metals and the metals immediately following the transition series. Two different groups of metals result from a consideration of halide complexes:[2]

Stability order, $F^- \gg Cl^- > Br^- > I^-$:

$$H^+, Fe^{3+}, In^{3+}, Ce^{3+}, U^{4+}, UO_2^{2+}, Zr^{4+},$$
$$Be^{2+}, Cu^{2+}, Zn^{2+}, Sn^{2+}, Al^{3+}, Th^{4+}, Pu^{4+}.$$

Stability order, $F^- \ll Cl^- < Br^- < I^-$:

$$Cu^+, Ag^+, Cd^{2+}, Hg^{2+}, Pb^{2+}, Pt^{2+},$$
$$Pd^{2+}, Au^{3+}, Tl^{3+}, Pd^{4+}, Pt^{4+}.$$

Ligands such as CN^-, CO, C_2H_4, NO_2^-, PR_3, AsR_3, SbR_3, R_2S, R_2Se and R_2Te form stable complexes primarily with transition metal ions containing d-orbital electrons. It will be noted that the latter group of ligands have vacant orbitals or orbitals that can be vacated to receive π electrons from the metal.[3]

When a metal ion equilibrates with reasonable rapidity with a ligand, it is possible to measure the equilibrium constants for complex formation. For example, in the $Hg^{2+} - Cl^-$ system,[4]

$$Hg^{2+} + Cl^- = HgCl^+ \qquad K_1 = 5.5 \times 10^6 \quad (4.1)$$

[1] N. V. Sidgwick, *J. Chem. Soc.*, 433 (1941).

[2] S. Ahrland, *Acta Chem. Scand.*, **10**, 723 (1956).

[3] L. Pauling, "The Nature of the Chemical Bond," 2nd ed., Cornell University Press, Ithaca, N. Y., 1948, pp. 250–8.

[4] L. G. Sillén, *Acta Chem. Scand.*, **3**, 539 (1949).

$$HgCl^+ + Cl^- = HgCl_2 \qquad K_2 = 3.0 \times 10^6 \quad (4.2)$$

$$HgCl_2 + Cl^- = HgCl_3^- \qquad K_3 = 7.1 \quad (4.3)$$

$$HgCl_3^- + Cl^- = HgCl_4^{2-} \qquad K_4 = 10.0 \quad (4.4)$$

LABILITY OF COMPLEXES

Of course, it is not enough to know whether or not a reaction is thermodynamically possible. The following substitution reaction has an equilibrium constant of 2×10^4,

$$[Co(NH_3)_6]^{3+} + Cl^- = [Co(NH_3)_5Cl]^{2+} + NH_3 \qquad (4.5)$$

and yet $[Co(NH_3)_6]Cl_3$ can be refluxed with 6 M hydrochloric acid for hours without any of the coordinated ammonia being displaced. One must heat the hexammine complex with concentrated hydrochloric acid in a sealed tube in order to effect reaction. Even the reverse reaction, the substitution of the chloride by ammonia, is very slow. This reaction will take place at a reasonable rate in concentrated ammonium hydroxide if activated charcoal is used as a catalyst.[5]

Fortunately, metal ions may be classified as to the "inertness" of their complexes. Taube[6] has discussed the hexacovalent complexes in which, according to the valence-bond theory, two d-orbitals of principal quantum number one less than that of the metal's valence electrons are used in bonding to the ligands (*e.g.*, $3d^24s4p^3$ hybridization). He pointed out that those complexes in which the metal ion has less than three unused electrons in the d-shell are "labile," whereas those in which the metal ion has three or more unused d-electrons are "inert." Thus, complexes of Sc^{3+}, Ti^{3+}, and V^{3+} are labile, and complexes of V^{2+}, Cr^{3+}, Co^{3+}, and Pt^{4+} are inert. Presumably all these complexes react by an S_N2 mechanism in which a seventh ligand must be added to the coordination sphere; such a process is aided when an empty d-orbital is available to the incoming ligand. As we shall see, however, some substitution reactions of this type are S_N1 in character, so this explanation is not generally applicable.

MECHANISMS OF SUBSTITUTION REACTIONS

The ligands of "inert" complexes undergo rearrangement slowly, so it is possible to isolate stereoisomers of some of these complexes. The most

[5] J. Bjerrum, "Metal Ammine Formation in Aqueous Solution," P. Haase and Son, Copenhagen, 1941.

[6] H. Taube, *Chem. Revs.*, **50**, 69 (1952).

important types of stereoisomerism are *cis-trans* isomerism (see Figure 4.1) and *optical* isomerism (see Figure 4.2).

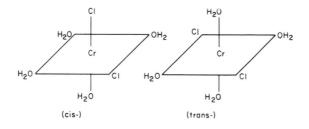

FIGURE 4.1.

The *cis-* and *trans-* Isomers of $Cr(H_2O)_4Cl_2^+$.

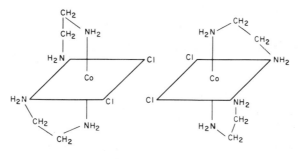

FIGURE 4.2.

Optical isomers of *cis*-$Co(en)_2Cl_2^+$.

Many substitution reactions of octahedral complexes proceed with retention of configuration; that is, the new ligand becomes attached in the same position as was occupied by the replaced ligand, the rest of the complex remaining unchanged. When such reactions are of S_N1 mechanism, it is presumed that a tetragonal pyramid intermediate is involved, as shown below.

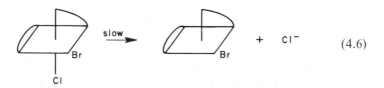

$$\text{slow} \qquad + \quad Cl^- \qquad (4.6)$$

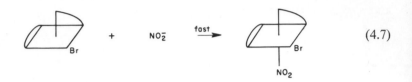

$$(4.7)$$

When such reactions are of S_N2 mechanism, it is presumed that a 7-coordinate intermediate is formed, as shown below.

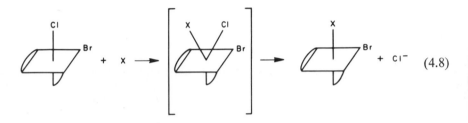

$$(4.8)$$

However, substitutions are occasionally accompanied by rearrangements. These reactions are generally of S_N1 mechanism, and it is believed that trigonal bipyramid intermediates are involved. For example, when *l-cis*-[Co en$_2$Cl$_2$]$^+$ is heated in methanol solution with radiochloride (Cl*$^-$), both *trans*-[Co en$_2$ClCl*]$^+$ and *dl-cis*-[Co en$_2$ClCl*]$^+$ are formed according to first-order rate laws.[7] Eventually, practically all the *cis*-[Co en$_2$ClCl*]$^+$ is converted to *trans*-[Co en$_2$ClCl*]$^+$. It has been suggested that the *trans*-product and the *dl-cis*-product are formed through a common intermediate. This intermediate would have to be optically symmetric to explain the fact that the rate of loss of optical activity equals the rate of radiochloride exchange. The intermediate A (Figure 4.3) seems more plausible than the intermediate B

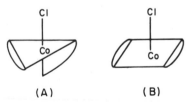

(A)   (B)

FIGURE 4.3.

Possible intermediates in the exchange of radiochloride with Co(en)$_2$Cl$_2$$^+$.

(Figure 4.3) because the experimental activation energy for the formation of the *trans*-isomer is greater than that for the formation of the *dl-cis*-isomer.

[7] D. D. Brown and R. S. Nyholm, *J. Chem. Soc.*, 2696 (1953).

Intermediate *A* would require less reorganization to form the *cis*-product than it would to form the *trans*-product. On the other hand, intermediate *B* more easily yields the *trans*-isomer than the *cis*-isomer. The proposed mechanism is outlined below:

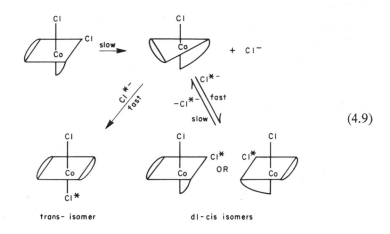

(4.9)

trans- isomer	dl - cis isomers

THE PREDICTION OF REACTION MECHANISMS

The synthetic chemist would like to be able to predict confidently which ligand (or ligands) is lost in a substitution reaction and what the configuration of the product is. Unfortunately, this ideal situation does not yet exist; however, there are certain tentative rules which can aid in such predictions.

Does the substitution proceed by an S_N1 or S_N2 mechanism? It has been noted that a small positive charge on the metal atom favors an S_N1 process, whereas a large positive charge favors an S_N2 displacement.[8] Cobalt(III) complexes which contain negative ligands with more than one lone electron pair (*e.g.*, NH_2^-, OH^-, Cl^-) are particularly prone to undergo S_N1 reactions. Complexes containing electron-withdrawing ligands such as NO_2^-, CN^-, and so on, are more likely to undergo S_N2 reactions. Whereas most cobalt(III) complexes react by S_N1 processes, platinum(IV) complexes react by S_N2 processes.

Which ligand is lost? In S_N1 reactions, the ligand which is held least strongly (thermodynamically) is usually lost. In S_N2 reactions, the situation is more complicated. A phenomenon known as the *trans*-effect often occurs in these cases. The *trans*-effect is explained at the end of this chapter.

[8] F. Basolo, *Record Chem. Prog., Kresge-Hooker Science Lib.*, **18**, 1 (1957).

Will a rearrangement occur? Presumably, rearrangements can only occur through S_N1 mechanisms which involve trigonal bipyramid intermediates. Such intermediates seem to be stabilized by negative ligands with more than one lone electron pair. This would explain why the acid hydrolyses of chloroamminecobalt(III) complexes take place largely with retention of configuration (through tetragonal pyramid intermediates), whereas the base hydrolyses take place primarily with rearrangement (through trigonal bipyramid intermediates).[8] Consider the acid and base hydrolyses of trans-$Co(en)_2(NH_3)Cl^{2+}$:

ACID HYDROLYSIS:

$$\textit{trans-}Co(en)_2(NH_3)Cl^{2+} \longrightarrow Co(en)_2NH_3{}^{3+} + Cl^- \qquad (4.10)$$

$$Co(en)_2NH_3{}^{3+} + H_2O \longrightarrow \textit{trans-}Co(en)_2(NH_3)H_2O^{3+} \qquad (4.11)$$

BASE HYDROLYSIS:

$$\textit{trans-}Co(en)_2(NH_3)Cl^{2+} + OH^- \rightleftharpoons \textit{trans-}Co(en)_2(NH_2)Cl^+ + H_2O \qquad (4.12)$$

$$\textit{trans-}Co(en)_2(NH_2)Cl^+ \longrightarrow Co(en)_2NH_2{}^{2+} + Cl^- \qquad (4.13)$$

$$Co(en)_2NH_2{}^{2+} + H_2O \longrightarrow \textit{cis-}Co(en)_2(NH_3)OH^{2+} \qquad (4.14)$$

THE *TRANS*-EFFECT[9]

Certain ligands labilize (make susceptible to substitution) groups in the *trans*-position. Various ligands may be compared as to their abilities in this respect. In the following list, the ligands are listed in the order of decreasing *trans*-effect.

$$CN^- > C_2H_4 > CO > NO_2{}^- > SC(NH_2)_2 > R_2S \sim PR_3 \sim I^- >$$
$$Br^- > Cl^- > F^- \sim NH_3 > OH^- > H_2O.$$

Consider the reaction of the tetrachloroplatinate(II) ion with two molecules of ammonia. After one molecule of ammonia has reacted, there are two kinds of chloride ions remaining in the complex: those which are *trans*-to each other, and that which is *trans*- to the ammonia. Now, chloride is more *trans*-directing than ammonia, and so the chlorides which are *trans*- to each other are labilized more than the chloride which is *trans*- to the ammonia.

[9] The reader is referred to J. V. Quagliano and L. Schubert (*Chem. Revs.*, **50**, 201 (1952)), for examples of the *trans*-effect and to F. Basolo and R. G. Pearson ("Mechanisms of Inorganic Reactions," John Wiley and Sons, New York, 1958) for a discussion of various theories of the *trans*-effect.

Hence, it is one of these labilized chlorides which is next displaced, forming *cis*-[Pt(NH$_3$)$_2$Cl$_2$].

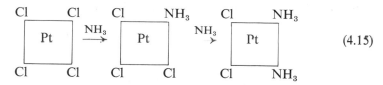

$$(4.15)$$

Now consider the reaction of the tetrammineplatinum(II) ion with two moles of chloride ion. After the displacement of one ammonia molecule, there remain two ammonias *trans*- to each other and the ammonia *trans*- to the chloride. The latter ammonia molecule is labilized by the chloride and is the next to be displaced, forming *trans*-[Pt(NH$_3$)$_2$Cl$_2$].

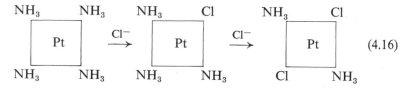

$$(4.16)$$

The *trans*-effect has been useful in the synthesis of many platinum(II) complexes, as well as some hexacoordinate complexes.

AN EXPLANATION OF THE *TRANS*-EFFECT

Let us assume that substitution reactions of Pt(II) complexes are bimolecular. It is reasonable that the entering group approaches the complex from one side of the plane over the group to be replaced. In the activated complex the leaving group will have moved down so that a trigonal bipyramid arrangement is achieved.

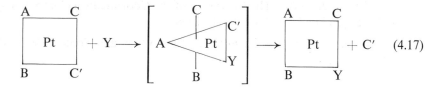

$$(4.17)$$

Now, it will be noted that the ligands with the largest *trans*-effects are just those which have vacant orbitals suitable for forming π-bonds. So we must explain why the more stable activated complex is that in which the ligand which more readily forms π-bonds is equatorial. The *d*-orbital of platinum which would be used in π-bonding to ligand A has four lobes in a plane perpendicular to that of the original complex, as shown in Figure 4.4. It will be noted that the two lobes directed toward C$'$ are pointed toward the positions occupied by Y and C′ in the activated complex. The activated complex will be stabilized by a reduction in the density of d electrons at these positions. This is exactly what happens when the d electrons are used in

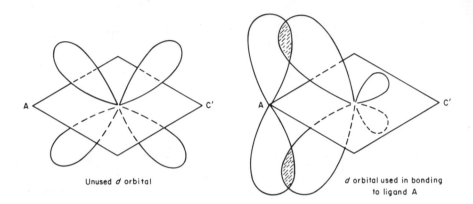

Unused d orbital

d orbital used in bonding to ligand A

FIGURE 4.4.

d_{xz} or d_{yz} orbital of a Pt(II) complex.

bonding to ligand A. The stronger the double-bonding, the lower is the electron density in the critical directions and the more *trans*-directing is the ligand.

BIBLIOGRAPHY

F. Basolo and R. G. Pearson, "Mechanisms of Inorganic Reactions," John Wiley and Sons, New York, 1958.

J. C. Bailar, Jr., Ed., "The Chemistry of the Coordination Compounds," Reinhold Publ. Corp., New York, 1956.

T. Moeller, "Inorganic Chemistry," John Wiley and Sons, New York, 1952, Chapter 7.

PROBLEMS

1. When *cis*-[Pt(NH$_3$)$_2$(NH$_2$OH)$_2$]$^{2+}$ is treated with HCl, [PtCl$_2$(NH$_3$)(NH$_2$OH)] is formed. Would you expect this product to be *cis*- or *trans*-? Since NH$_2$OH is a poorer complexing agent than NH$_3$, why doesn't [PtCl$_2$(NH$_3$)$_2$] form?

2. Using the *trans*-effect, predict the product of the reaction of two moles of ethylenediamine with one mole of PtCl$_6^{2-}$.

3. Suggest plausible mechanisms for the following reactions of cobalt(III) complexes.

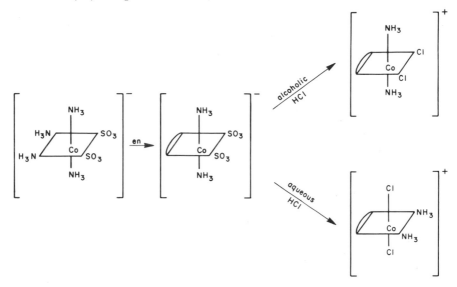

Chemistry of Metal-Ammonia Solutions[10]

The alkali metals and the alkaline earth metals heavier than magnesium readily dissolve in liquid ammonia to form highly reactive, blue solutions. Although the nature of the concentrated solutions is somewhat uncertain, we know that in dilute solutions the metals ionize to give ammoniated metal ions and ammoniated electrons. The reducing properties of metal-ammonia solutions may be attributed to the ammoniated electrons.

Simple electron addition without bond rupture. Some species undergo reduction in metal-ammonia solutions by adding an electron. For example, potassium manganate(VI) may be prepared by reducing a solution of potassium permanganate with potassium:

$$e_{am}^- + MnO_4^- \longrightarrow MnO_4^{2-}. \qquad (4.18)$$

Oxygen, when in excess, will react to form the superoxide ion:

$$e_{am}^- + O_2 \longrightarrow O_2^-. \qquad (4.19)$$

The trimethyl tin radical may be reduced to the corresponding anion:

$$e_{am}^- + (CH_3)_3Sn\cdot \longrightarrow (CH_3)_3Sn\colon^-. \qquad (4.20)$$

[10] For a discussion of the physical properties of metal-ammonia solutions, see W. L. Jolly, *Progress in Inorganic Chemistry*, **1**, 235 (1959).

Bond rupture by the addition of one electron. When a bond is broken by the addition of an electron, an anion and a radical are probably formed in the first step. The following reaction is an unusual case in which the radical formed is stable:

$$e_{am}^- + (C_2H_5)_3SnBr \longrightarrow (C_2H_5)_3Sn\cdot + Br^-. \tag{4.21}$$

Usually the radical undergoes dimerization, as in the following examples.

$$e_{am}^- + NH_4^+ \longrightarrow NH_3 + {}^1/_2\, H_2 \tag{4.22}$$

$$e_{am}^- + AsH_3 \longrightarrow AsH_2^- + {}^1/_2\, H_2 \tag{4.23}$$

$$e_{am}^- + RC\equiv CH \longrightarrow RC\equiv C:^- + {}^1/_2\, H_2 \tag{4.24}$$

$$e_{am}^- + R_2S \longrightarrow RS^- + {}^1/_2\, R{-}R. \tag{4.25}$$

Bond rupture by the addition of two electrons. When a bond is ruptured by the addition of two electrons, either two anions or a "di-anion" form:

$$2\,e_{am}^- + Ge_2H_6 \longrightarrow 2\, GeH_3^- \tag{4.26}$$

$$2\,e_{am}^- + C_6H_5NHNH_2 \longrightarrow C_6H_5NH^- + NH_2^- \tag{4.27}$$

$$2\,e_{am}^- + C_6H_5{-}N{=}O \longrightarrow C_6H_5{-}N^-{-}O^-. \tag{4.28}$$

However, one of the anions usually undergoes ammonolysis, as in the following examples.

$$2\,e_{am}^- + N\equiv N^+{-}O^- \longrightarrow N_2 + O^{2-}$$
$$\downarrow NH_3 \tag{4.29}$$
$$OH^- + NH_2^-$$

$$2\,e_{am}^- + N\equiv C{-}O^- \longrightarrow CN^- + O^{2-}$$
$$\downarrow NH_3 \tag{4.30}$$
$$OH^- + NH_2^-$$

$$2\,e_{am}^- + Br{-}C_2H_5 \longrightarrow Br^- + C_2H_5^-$$
$$\downarrow NH_3 \tag{4.31}$$
$$C_2H_6 + NH_2^-$$

$$2\,e_{am}^- + RCH{=}CH_2 \longrightarrow RCH{-}CH_2^{2-}$$
$$\downarrow 2\,NH_3 \tag{4.32}$$
$$RCH_2{-}CH_3 + 2\, NH_2^-.$$

Factors influencing the course of reduction. Sometimes the course of a metal-ammonia reduction may be influenced by the relative concentrations of reactant and metal or by the presence of acidic species such as ammonium salts or alcohols.

Thus, if sodium is added to a solution of acetylene (or one of its mono-substituted derivatives) at such a rate that the acetylene is always in excess, a solution of sodium acetylide is formed:

$$e_{am}^- + RC{\equiv}CH \longrightarrow RC{\equiv}C^- + {}^1/_2\,H_2. \tag{4.33}$$

If the acetylene is allowed to react with excess sodium, the salt of the corresponding olefin is formed.

$$2\,e_{am}^- + RC{\equiv}CH \longrightarrow RC{=}CH^{2-}. \tag{4.34}$$

The olefin may be released by the addition of an ammonium salt.[11]

$$RC{=}CH^{2-} + 2\,NH_4^+ \longrightarrow RCH{=}CH_2 + 2\,NH_3. \tag{4.35}$$

The disodium salt of biphosphine ($Na_2H_2P_2$) is unaffected by dissolved sodium in liquid ammonia. However, if an ammonium salt is added to a solution of $Na_2H_2P_2$ and sodium, reduction to sodium dihydrogen phosphide ($NaPH_2$) occurs.[12,13] Apparently only biphosphine, not its disodium salt, undergoes cleavage by electrons.

$$P_2H_2^{2-} \xrightarrow{2\,NH_4^+} P_2H_4 \xrightarrow{2e^-} 2\,PH_2^-. \tag{4.36}$$

If an excess of ammonium salt is added, phosphine is evolved.

$$PH_2^- + NH_4^+ \longrightarrow PH_3 + NH_3. \tag{4.37}$$

BIBLIOGRAPHY

L. F. Audrieth and J. Kleinberg, "Non-Aqueous Solvents," John Wiley and Sons, New York, 1953, Chapter 6.

G. W. Watt, *Chem. Revs.*, **46**, 289, 317 (1950); *J. Chem. Education*, **34**, 538 (1957).

A. J. Birch, *Quart. Rev.*, **4**, 69 (1950).

PROBLEMS

Explain the following facts.

1. When nitrous oxide is passed into a potassium-ammonia solution, nitrogen is evolved according to equation 4.29, but also potassium azide, KN_3, forms in an amount corresponding to one-quarter the amount of potassium oxidized.

---

[11] G. W. Watt, *Chem. Revs.*, **46**, 317 (1950).
[12] E. C. Evers, E. H. Street, Jr., and S. L. Jung, *J. Am. Chem. Soc.*, **73**, 5088 (1951).
[13] P. Royen and W. Zschaage, *Z. Naturforsch.*, **8b**, 777 (1953).

2. Ordinarily, a sodium-ammonia solution reduces nitroguanidine

$$\text{NH}$$
$$\|$$

(H_2N—C—NH—NO_2) to cyanamide and nitrogen. However, if the reduction is carried out in acid solution, the principal product is aminoguanidine.

3. A solution of tetraethylammonium ((C_2H_5)$_4$N) in ammonia decomposes to triethylamine, ethylene, ethane, and hydrogen.

Hydride Syntheses

Hydrides may be roughly classified into four groups: saline hydrides (such as LiH), interstitial hydrides (such as TiH_2), polymeric hydrides (such as (AlH_3)$_x$), and volatile hydrides (such as Si_2H_6). A wide variety of synthetic methods has been used for preparing hydrides; some of these methods are discussed below.

Reaction with molecular hydrogen. All of the saline hydrides and most of the interstitial hydrides are conveniently prepared by direct reaction of the metal with hydrogen gas. The phase diagram for the lithium-hydrogen system is given in Figure 4.5. When a small amount of hydrogen reacts with molten lithium around 700°, a solution of lithium hydride in lithium forms. If enough hydrogen is allowed to react, the amount of lithium hydride formed exceeds that which is soluble in the molten lithium. Then two liquid phases are formed: a saturated solution of lithium hydride in lithium and a saturated solution of lithium in lithium hydride. Both phases are present until sufficient hydrogen has reacted to consume the lithium-rich phase. The composition of the hydrogen-rich phase depends upon the pressure of the hydrogen in equilibrium with it. It will be noticed from Figure 4.5 that, as the composition of stoichiometric LiH is approached, the dissociation pressure goes to extremely high values. As expected, the miscibility gap becomes shorter at higher temperatures. Presumably, if one went to a high enough temperature and a high enough pressure, a critical point would be reached above which only one phase would exist for all Li-H compositions.

Solid-solid miscibility gaps have been observed for various metal-hydrogen systems such as the Ti-H system,[14] the Zr-H system,[15] and the U-H system.[16] Some of the plateaus in the pressure *vs.* composition plots may be interpreted in terms of equilibria between metal phases saturated with inter-

[14] R. M. Haag and F. J. Shipko, *J. Am. Chem. Soc.*, **78**, 5155 (1956).
[15] S. L. H. Martin and A. L. G. Rees, *Trans. Faraday Soc.*, **50**, 343 (1954).
[16] F. H. Spedding, *et al.*, *Nucleonics*, **4**, 4 (1949).

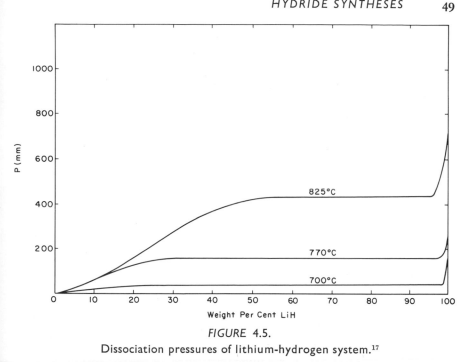

FIGURE 4.5.

Dissociation pressures of lithium-hydrogen system.[17]

stitial hydrogen and hydride phases saturated with hydrogen vacancies. Others result from equilibria between metal phases of different crystal structure, each phase containing interstitial hydrogen.

Reaction with atomic hydrogen.[18] When molecular hydrogen is passed through a suitable electric discharge, an appreciable fraction of the molecules are dissociated to atoms. The atoms recombine with remarkable slowness and it is possible to direct a stream of atomic hydrogen into various parts of a glass system. By bringing atomic hydrogen into contact with the appropriate element, one may prepare practically any known hydride. However, the method is ordinarily not a practical one.

Electrolytic reduction. In this category, we include not only cathodic reduction, but also reduction by electropositive metals, since the mechanisms of reduction are probably similar. For example, arsine (AsH_3) may be prepared either by cathodic reduction of an arsenious acid solution,

$$6\,e^- + H_3AsO_3 + 6\,H^+ = AsH_3 + 3\,H_2O \qquad (4.38)$$

[17] L. L. Hill, Thesis, University of Chicago, 1938, and M. R. J. Perlow, Thesis, University of Chicago, 1941; see C. E. Messer, E. B. Damon, and P. C. Maybury, Report NYO-3958, issued Dec. 1, 1955 under contract AT(30–1)1410.

[18] See E. B. Maxted, "Modern Advances in Inorganic Chemistry," Oxford University Press, 1947, pp. 80–84.

or by addition of magnesium chips to a solution of arsenic trichloride containing excess hydrochloric acid.

$$3 \text{ Mg} + \text{AsCl}_3 + 3 \text{ H}^+ = \text{AsH}_3 + 3 \text{ Mg}^{2+} + 3 \text{ Cl}^-. \tag{4.39}$$

Other hydrides which may be prepared by analogous procedures are PH_3, SbH_3, BiH_3, GeH_4, SnH_4, P_2H_4, and so on.

Solvolysis of metal "-ide" salts. When calcium phosphide, Ca_3P_2, is allowed to react with aqueous acid, both phosphine, PH_3, and biphosphine, P_2H_4, are formed.

$$Ca_3P_2 + 6 \text{ H}^+ = 3 \text{ Ca}^{2+} + 2 \text{ PH}_3 \tag{4.40}$$

$$Ca_3P_2 + 6 \text{ H}^+ = 3 \text{ Ca}^{2+} + P_2H_4 + H_2. \tag{4.41}$$

Similar hydrolyses (more commonly with the appropriate magnesium salts) may be used for preparing most of the hydrides of the elements in Groups IVA and VA, as well as many of the boron hydrides. It has been observed that better yields of silanes,[19] germanes,[20] and arsine[21] are obtained by treating the appropriate magnesium or sodium salts with acidic liquid ammonia solutions (solutions of NH_4Br in NH_3) rather than with aqueous acid. In fact, good yields of germane are obtained by the solvolysis of magnesium germanide in solutions of hydrazinium chloride in anhydrous hydrazine.[22]

Reduction with $LiAlH_4$ and hydroborates. Lithium hydroaluminate may be used for the preparation of practically all hydrides except the interstitial hydrides. Lithium hydroaluminate reacts with the halides of elements of equal or greater electronegativity than aluminum, and with the alkyls of elements more electropositive than aluminum.[23] (See Table 4.6.) The following reactions are typical:

$$\text{LiAlH}_4 + \text{GeCl}_4 \xrightarrow{\text{ether}} \text{GeH}_4 + \text{LiCl} + \text{AlCl}_3 \tag{4.42}$$

$$2 \text{ LiAlH}_4 + \text{Zn(CH}_3)_2 \xrightarrow{\text{ether}} \text{ZnH}_2 + 2 \text{ LiAlH}_3\text{CH}_3. \tag{4.43}$$

Lithium hydroaluminate has the disadvantage that it reacts rapidly with moisture and oxygen and that its reactions must be carried out in aprotic solvents.

Sodium and potassium hydroborate, on the other hand, react slowly with water and oxygen, and aqueous solutions may be used. Aqueous

[19] Johnson and Isenberg, *J. Am. Chem. Soc.*, **57**, 1349 (1935).
[20] Kraus and Carney, *J. Am. Chem. Soc.*, **56**, 765 (1934).
[21] W. C. Johnson and A. Pechukas, *J. Am. Chem. Soc.*, **59**, 2065 (1937).
[22] F. Fehér and J. Cremer, *Z. anorg. allgem. Chem.*, **297**, 14 (1958).
[23] T. Wartik and H. I. Schlesinger, *J. Am. Chem. Soc.*, **75**, 835 (1953).

TABLE 4.6

Reactions with LiAlH$_4$

	Alkyls	Halides
Group I Elements (Li, Na, etc.)	Hydride Formation	No Reaction
Group II Elements (Be, Mg, Zn, Cd)	,,	,,
Group III Elements (B, Al, Ga)	Formation of LiMRH$_3$	Hydride Formation
Group IV Elements (C, Si, Ge, etc.)	No Reaction	,,
Group V Elements (P, As, Sb)	,,	,,
Group VI Elements (O, S, etc.)	,,	?

hydroborate solutions have been used for the preparation of germane,[24] stannane,[25] arsine,[26] and stibine.[27] The following reactions are typical.

$$3\ BH_4^- + 4\ Sn^{2+} + 9\ H_2O \longrightarrow 4\ SnH_4 + 3\ H_3BO_3 + 5\ H^+ \qquad (4.44)$$

$$3\ BH_4^- + 4\ H_3AsO_3 + 3\ H^+ \longrightarrow 4\ AsH_3 + 3\ H_3BO_3 + 3\ H_2O. \qquad (4.45)$$

Thermal decomposition of metal alkyls. Certain metal alkyls decompose upon heating to give the corresponding metal hydrides. For example, the ethyl derivatives of lithium, sodium, and magnesium decompose to give ethylene and the appropriate hydride.[28]

$$CH_3{-}CH_2{-}Li \xrightarrow{\ \Delta\ } CH_2{=}CH_2 + LiH. \qquad (4.46)$$

Di-tert-butylberyllium decomposes to give isobutene and beryllium hydride.

Disproportionation of hydrides. Certain hydrides decompose spontaneously, or on heating, to give two or more hydrides of lower and higher molecular weights. For example, biphosphine[29] and biarsine[30] decompose according to the following type of reaction,

$$5\ P_2H_4 \longrightarrow 6\ PH_3 + \frac{2}{x}\ (P_2H)_x. \qquad (4.47)$$

[24] T. S. Piper and M. K. Wilson, *J. Inorg. Nuclear Chem.*, **4**, 22 (1957); E. D. Macklen, *J. Chem. Soc.*, 1989 (1959).

[25] G. W. Schaeffer and M. Emilius, *J. Am. Chem. Soc.*, **76**, 1203 (1954).

[26] Unpublished observations by the author.

[27] L. Berka, T. Briggs, M. Millard, and W. Jolly, *J. Inorg. Nuclear Chem.*, **14**, 190 (1960).

[28] G. E. Coates, "Organo-Metallic Compounds," Methuen and Co., Ltd., London, 1956.

[29] R. Schenck and E. Buck, *Chem. Ber.*, **37**, 915 (1904); E. C. Evers and E. H. Street, Jr., *J. Am. Chem. Soc.*, **78**, 5726 (1956).

[30] R. Nast, *Chem. Ber.*, **81**, 271 (1948).

When the vapors of tetraborane are heated to 100–200°, diborane, penta-borane(9), and small amounts of other hydrides are formed.[31]

$$B_4H_{10} \longrightarrow B_2H_6 + B_5H_9 + \cdots \qquad (4.48)$$

Hydride synthesis in an electric discharge. When either ammonia, phosphine, or arsine is passed through a silent electric discharge, either hydrazine, biphosphine, or biarsine, respectively, is formed along with hydrogen.[32, 33] When diborane is similarly treated, H_2, B_4H_{10}, B_5H_9, B_5H_{11}, and small amounts of B_6H_{10} and B_9H_{15} are formed.[34]

Miscellaneous methods. Rapid, uncatalyzed reactions of molecular hydrogen at room temperature are very unusual. One example is the reaction of hydrogen with diboron tetrachloride to give diborane,[35]

$$3 H_2 + 3 B_2Cl_4 \longrightarrow B_2H_6 + 4 BCl_3. \qquad (4.49)$$

Another is the reaction of hydrogen with the alkali metal phenyls.[28]

$$H_2 + KC_6H_5 \longrightarrow KH + C_6H_6 \qquad (4.50)$$

The relative rates of the latter reactions illustrate the order of reactivities of the alkali metal aryls, since the reaction rate increases in the order $Li < Na < K < Rb < Cs$.

The solid hydride CuH may be prepared by the reduction of the cupric ion by hypophosphite in aqueous solution.[36]

Hydrazine may be prepared by the oxidation of ammonia by hypochlorite.

$$2 NH_3 + OCl^- \longrightarrow N_2H_4 + Cl^- + H_2O. \qquad (4.51)$$

Phosphine may be prepared by the disproportionation of phosphorus in hot alkaline solutions.

$$P_4 + 3 OH^- + 3 H_2O \longrightarrow PH_3 + 3 H_2PO_2^-. \qquad (4.52)$$

The sulfanes H_2S_5, H_2S_6, H_2S_7 and H_2S_8 have been prepared by condensation reactions of the type[37]

$$2 H_2S_2 + S_nCl_2 \longrightarrow H_2S_{n+4} + 2 HCl. \qquad (4.53)$$

[31] A. Stock, "Hydrides of Boron and Silicon," Cornell University Press, Ithaca, N. Y., 1933.

[32] A. Koenig and T. Brings, *Z. phys. Chem., Bodenstein Festband*, 541 (1931).

[33] W. L. Jolly, L. B. Anderson, and R. T. Beltrami, *J. Am. Chem. Soc.*, **79**, 2443 (1957).

[34] W. V. Kotlensky and R. Schaeffer, *J. Am. Chem. Soc.*, **80**, 4517 (1958).

[35] G. Urry, T. Wartik, R. E. Moore, and H. I. Schlesinger, *J. Am. Chem. Soc.*, **76**, 5293 (1954).

[36] G. Brauer, "Handbuch der Präparativen Anorganischen Chemie," Ferdinand Enke, Stuttgart, 1954, p. 751.

[37] F. Fehér and G. Winkhaus, *Z. anorg. allgem. Chem.*, **288**, 123 (1956).

BIBLIOGRAPHY

D. T. Hurd, "An Introduction to the Chemistry of the Hydrides," John Wiley and Sons, New York, 1952.

T. Moeller, "Inorganic Chemistry," John Wiley and Sons., New York, 1952, pp. 403–416.

PROBLEMS

1. What products would you expect if an equimolar mixture of $LiBH_4$ and $(CH_3)_3NHCl$ were heated?

2. Suggest an explanation for the fact that better yields of silanes are obtained from the ammonolysis of magnesium silicide in liquid ammonia than from the corresponding hydrolysis in water. On the other hand, why can boron hydrides be obtained from the aqueous hydrolysis of magnesium boride and not from the corresponding liquid ammonia ammonolysis?

3. Why cannot silanes be prepared by the reaction of silicon with molecular hydrogen, analogously to the preparation of lithium hydride?

CHAPTER 5

STRUCTURE FROM CHEMICAL DATA

A chemist is very seldom satisfied with simply preparing a compound for the first time. The question immediately arises: what is the structure of this new compound? So the chemist then proceeds to collect sufficient data to determine the structure. These data may be roughly classified into three categories: *"microscopic" measurements*, *"macroscopic" measurements*, and *chemical data*.

"Microscopic" measurements are defined here as those measurements which give detailed, specific structural information. Under appropriate circumstances, the following techniques yield such information:

> X-ray diffraction
> Electron diffraction
> Neutron diffraction
> Spectroscopy—
>> Microwave
>> Infrared
>> Raman
>> Visible-ultraviolet
>> Mass spectroscopy
> Nuclear magnetic resonance
> Electron magnetic resonance

"*Macroscopic*" *measurements* are defined here as physical measurements which cannot uniquely determine molecular structure but which can establish the general structure type. Measurements of gross physical properties such as the following fit this category:

> Vapor pressure
> Melting point
> Viscosity
> Density
> Dielectric constant
> Surface tension
> Refractive index
> Electrical conductivity
> Optical rotation

By *chemical data*, we mean information (often obtained with the aid of "macroscopic" measurements) about chemical reactions involving the compound whose structure is sought. Such information, if carefully interpreted, may sometimes be used to choose one structure from several alternative structures.

In this chapter, we shall discuss the application of chemical data to various structural problems.

Discriminative Analysis

Many molecules and ions contain more than one atom of a particular element. In determining the structure of such a species, it is very helpful to know whether or not all the atoms of the element are equivalent. For example, all the hydrogens in ethane (C_2H_6) are equivalent. On the other hand, there are two kinds of hydrogen atoms—four of one kind and two of another—in diborane (B_2H_6). Hence, the "hydrogen bridge" structure for diborane is quite reasonable:

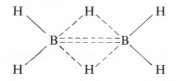

In the following paragraphs, we shall examine some of the types of chemical data which have been used to distinguish two or more kinds of atoms of the same element in compounds.

DISCRIMINATION BY MEANS OF THERMODYNAMIC PROPERTIES

The structures of many phosphorus oxy-acids have been deduced from a knowledge of the relative acidities of the protons. For example, only two of the hydrogens in phosphorous acid (H_3PO_3) may be titrated with alkali. Hence, the following structure has been proposed for the acid.

The chain polyphosphoric acids consist of chains of —O—PO(OH)— groups, as shown below:

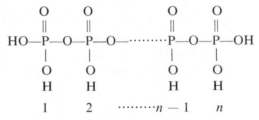

Theoretically, the chain length could be ascertained from a knowledge of the ratio of total hydrogen to total phosphorus, but for chains with n greater than 4 or 5, ordinary analytical precision leads to very uncertain values for n. A simpler, more accurate procedure takes advantage of the fact that, after one of the two identical protons on each terminal —$PO(OH)_2$ group dissociates, the remaining proton dissociates with much greater difficulty. Thus there are apparently n strongly acidic protons per chain (one per phosphorus atom) and two weakly acidic protons per chain (one at each end). The "strong" hydrogens have ionization constants around 10^{-2}–10^{-3} and the "weak" hydrogens have ionization constants around 10^{-7}–10^{-8}. Thus they may be readily distinguished by a pH titration.[1] Triphosphoric acid, for example, gives a titration curve with two main inflections, spaced such as to indicate that the ratio of "weak" to "strong" hydrogens is 2:3.

DISCRIMINATION BY MEANS OF KINETIC PROPERTIES

When silver nitrate is added to a freshly prepared solution of anhydrous chromium(III) chloride in water, only one-third of the chlorine is precipitated as silver chloride. Therefore it is believed that two of the chloride ions

[1] E. J. Griffith, *J. Am. Chem. Soc.*, **79**, 509 (1957).

are coordinated directly to the chromium atom and that the other is ionized. The formula of the complex ion is $Cr(H_2O)_4Cl_2^+$, and the salt $[Cr(H_2O)_4Cl_2]$-$Cl \cdot 2H_2O$ may be crystallized from a solution of $CrCl_3$ in water.

DISCRIMINATION BY MEANS OF ISOTOPIC LABELING

Tracer techniques offer two simple methods for determining the equivalence or non-equivalence of atoms in a molecule. (1) The compound may be synthesized in such a way that only part of the atoms in question are labeled. The compound is then degraded to two different species containing these atoms. If the concentrations of labeled atoms are markedly different in these two species, it may be concluded that the atoms in the original compound were non-equivalent. (2) If part of the atoms in a compound exchange with another species more rapidly than the other part, it may be concluded that the atoms in the compound are non-equivalent. Examples of each of these methods are discussed below.

Synthesis-decomposition method. The thiosulfate ion, $S_2O_3^{2-}$, might be formulated as either

$$O—S—O—S—O \quad \text{or} \quad \overset{\displaystyle O}{\underset{\displaystyle O}{\overset{|}{\underset{|}{O—S—S}}}}$$

In the first structure, the two sulfur atoms are equivalent; whereas in the second structure they are non-equivalent. The second structure is compatible with the observation that, when thiosulfate is prepared from sulfite and radio-active sulfur and then decomposed to sulfide and sulfate (by decomposition of the silver salt), the radioactivity appears only in the sulfide.[2]

$$S^* + SO_3^{2-} \longrightarrow S^*SO_3^{2-} \xrightarrow{Ag^+} Ag_2S^*SO_3 \tag{5.1}$$

$$Ag_2S^*SO_3 + H_2O \xrightarrow{\Delta} Ag_2S^* + 2\,H^+ + SO_4^{2-}. \tag{5.2}$$

The equivalence of the lead atoms in lead sesquioxide, Pb_2O_3, was investigated by preparing Pb_2O_3 with radioactive plumbite and ordinary plumbate:[3]

$$HPb^*O_2^- + PbO_3^{2-} + H_2O = Pb^*PbO_3 + 3\,OH^-. \tag{5.3}$$

The precipitate was allowed to stand for three hours and then decomposed with 12 M KOH:

$$Pb^*PbO_3 + 4\,OH^- = PbO_3^{2-} + Pb^*O_2^{2-} + 2\,H_2O. \tag{5.4}$$

[2] E. B. Andersen, *Z. physik. Chem.*, **B32**, 237 (1936).
[3] E. Zintl and A. Rauch, *Ber.*, **57**, 1739 (1924).

The plumbate was separated by the precipitation of barium plumbate. Since practically all the activity was found in the plumbite fraction, it was concluded that Pb_2O_3 may be regarded as lead(II) metaplumbate(IV), $Pb(PbO_3)$.

Exchange-rate method. The equivalence of the iodine atoms in diphenyliodonium iodide was studied by allowing the normal compound to exchange with radioactive iodide ion.[4] The material was then treated with silver oxide and the organic product was found to be inactive:

$$2(C_6H_5)_2I_2* + Ag_2O + H_2O = 2(C_6H_5)_2IOH + 2\ AgI*. \qquad (5.5)$$

It is apparent that the iodide exchanged with only one of the iodine atoms of diphenyliodonium iodide. These results are in agreement with the structure $[C_6H_5\!-\!I^+\!-\!C_6H_5]I^-$.

Preparation of Isomers

In the following paragraphs, we shall examine the structural information which may be obtained from compounds which exhibit isomerism.

OPTICAL ISOMERS

Hexacovalent coordination compounds of the types $MX_2Y_2Z_2$, $M(AA)X_2Y_2$,[5] $M(AA)_2X_2$,[5] $M(AA)(BB)X_2$,[5] $M(AA)X_2YZ$,[5] and so on possess certain isomeric forms unique in that they may be resolved into optical antipodes. For example, [Co en$_2$Cl$_2$]Cl has been found to exist in two forms. One is green and the other is violet. Certainly one of these must correspond to a *trans*-configuration for the chlorines and the other to a *cis*-configuration. It has been unequivocally demonstrated that the violet form is the *cis*-isomer, because when it is treated with a solution of ammonium d-α-bromo-camphor-π-sulfonate, one may crystallize out a salt which, when treated with hydrochloric acid, yields optically active [Co en$_2$Cl$_2$]Cl.[6] It will be noted that the *trans*-isomer possesses a plane of symmetry and cannot be separated into optical antipodes.

However, it must never be concluded that an isomer possesses a plane of symmetry simply because an attempt to resolve it was unsuccessful. Another technique for resolution might prove successful.

[4] F. Juliusberger, B. Topley, and J. Weiss, *J. Chem. Soc.*, 1295 (1935).

[5] (AA) and (BB) represent bidentate ligands, *i.e.*, ligands, such as ethylenediamine, which may coordinate to a metal atom at two adjacent positions.

[6] J. C. Bailar, Jr., and C. L. Rollinson, *Inorg. Syntheses*, **2**, 222 (1946).

POSITIONAL ISOMERS

No more than four of the six hydrogen atoms of diborane have been replaced with methyl groups.[7] Only five methyl derivatives are known: monomethyl diborane, trimethyl diborane, tetramethyl diborane, and two isomers of dimethyl diborane. These facts suggest that two of the six hydrogen atoms in diborane are bound differently from the others and support the hydrogen-bridge model for diborane. It will be noted that, if diborane had an ethane-like structure and if there were no steric effects preventing complete substitution, one would expect nine different methyl derivatives.

Principle of "Retention of Configuration"

Chemists have long made use of the fact that when an organic compound reacts, most of the bonds between the atoms are unaffected. In fact, in most organic reactions, the minimum structural change consonant with the empirical change occurs. The latter generalization has been of great help in structure determinations. We shall consider several examples from the field of inorganic chemistry in which this generalization has been useful in the assignment of structure.

Two isomers of dichlorobis(ethylenediamine)chromium(III) chloride (a violet form and a green form) are known. In Figure 5.1, the reactions used to assign the *cis*-configuration to the violet form and the *trans*-configuration to the green form are represented schematically.[8] It will be noted that the chloride ions in the *trans*-complex cannot be replaced by the oxalate ion because the oxalate ion cannot span the *trans*-positions. Similarly, the *trans*-form of [Cr en$_2$(H$_2$O)(OH)]Cl$_2$ will not yield the binuclear complex [Cr$_2$en$_4$(OH)$_2$]Cl$_4$ because it is geometrically impossible to link two octahedra through two groups which are *trans*- in each octahedron. The reader will appreciate that, in view of the many rearrangements which coordination compounds are known to undergo (see Chapter 4), structure assignments of this type are very tentative.

It is possible to prepare at least two isomers of trimethylborazine, B$_3$N$_3$H$_3$(CH$_3$)$_3$. One isomer, with a boiling point of 133° and a melting point of $-7.5°$, may be prepared by heating a mixture of methyl-ammonium chloride and lithium borohydride.[9] Another isomer, with a boiling point of 129° and a melting point of 31.5° may be prepared by heating a mixture of

[7] H. I. Schlesinger and A. B. Burg., *Chem. Revs.*, **31**, 1 (1942).
[8] P. Pfeiffer, *Z. anorg. Chem.*, **56**, 261 (1908).
[9] G. W. Schaeffer and E. R. Anderson, *J. Am. Chem. Soc.*, **71**, 2143 (1949).

FIGURE 5.I

Transformations among Bisethylenediamine Chromium(III) Complexes

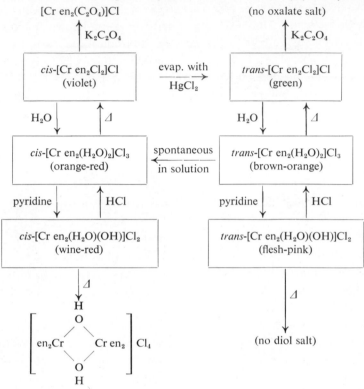

boron trimethyl and borazine.[10] If we assume that, in each of these reactions, a minimum number of bonds is broken, then we may assign structures to the isomers. The first compound is N-trimethylborazine and the second is B-trimethylborazine.

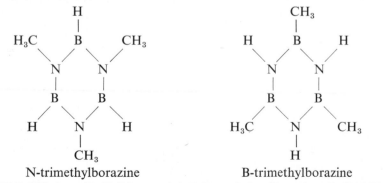

N-trimethylborazine   B-trimethylborazine

[10] H. I. Schlesinger, D. M. Ritter, and A. B. Burg, *J. Am. Chem. Soc.*, **60**, 1296 (1938).

These deductions have been corroborated by the differences in the products of hydrolysis of the compounds. The first compound gives three moles of hydrogen upon hydrolysis, whereas the second gives essentially none.

The principle of "retention of configuration" is only a rough guide. It seems to hold reasonably well with compounds of elements in the first row of the periodic table, but one should be skeptical of its application to other compounds, particularly those involving d-orbitals. For example, when the hypophosphate ion, $P_2O_6^{4-}$, is oxidized by bromine in aqueous bicarbonate solution, the diphosphate ion, $^{2-}O_3P-O-PO_3^{2-}$, is formed. This observation was once interpreted as an indication of the asymmetric structure, $^{2-}O_3P-O-PO_2^{2-}$, for the hypophosphate ion.[11] It was considered unlikely that the species contained a P—P bond, as in $^{2-}O_3P-PO_3^{2-}$, because it was thought that the oxidizing species would break the P—P bond and give orthophosphate as the sole product. However, several physical techniques have definitely shown that the last structure is correct.[12] If we assume that, in an intermediate step of the oxidation, the phosphorus atoms are pentacovalent (by use of d-orbitals), there is no difficulty in explaining the formation of diphosphate.

Hypothetical intermediate in oxidation of hypophosphate

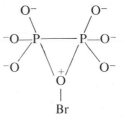

How Structures "Change with Time"

It is interesting to trace the histories of certain complicated compounds whose structures have been elucidated only very slowly. The following examples demonstrate the pitfalls one may fall into by relying on scanty data.

DIBORANE DIAMMONIATE

When diborane is allowed to react with excess ammonia at temperatures below $-80°$, a diammoniate of composition $B_2H_6 \cdot 2NH_3$ forms. A number of structures have been proposed for this compound, some of which are represented in Table 5.1. Structure I is certainly not correct, since a material

[11] B. Blaser and P. Halpern, *Z. anorg. allgem. Chem.*, **215**, 33 (1933).

[12] J. R. Van Wazer, "Phosphorus and its Compounds," Interscience Publishers, New York, 1958.

TABLE 5.1

Proposed Structures for "Diborane Diammoniate"

I	$H_3B:NH_3$	Ammonia-borane adduct
II	$(NH_4)_2B_2H_4$	Ammonium tetrahydrodiborate (2^-)
III	$NH_4(H_3B:NH_2:BH_3)$	Ammonium μ-amidohexahydrodiborate (1^-)
IV	$(NH_4)_2NH(BH_3)_3$	Ammonium tris(borane)hydronitrate (2^-)
V	$NH_4 \cdot BH_2NH_2 \cdot BH_4$	"Ammonium hydroborate + aminoborane"
VIA	$(H_3N:BH_2:NH_3)BH_4$	Diamminedihydroboron (1^+) hydroborate
VIB	$HB(NH_3)_3(BH_4)_2$	Triamminehydroboron (2^+) hydroborate

with this structure has been prepared by another method and has been found to possess properties entirely different from those of "diborane diammoniate."[13] (For example, ammonia-borane is quite volatile, whereas "diborane diammoniate" is non-volatile.) Structure II was proposed by Wiberg[14] to explain the observed acid character of liquid-ammonia solutions of the diammoniate, but quantitative studies have shown that, in fresh cold solutions, only one equivalent of ammonium ion is present per mole of diborane used,[15] and so Structure III was proposed. (Thus, when a cold solution of the diammoniate is allowed to react with excess sodium in ammonia, one equivalent of hydrogen is evolved.) However, from relatively warm solutions of the diammoniate, a total of about 1.33 equivalents of hydrogen are evolved per mole of ammoniate, and it has been suggested that Structure III undergoes rearrangement to Structure IV.[16] When the liquid ammonia is evaporated after allowing one gram-atom of sodium to react with a mole of diammoniate in ammonia, sodium hydroborate, $NaBH_4$, and aminoborane, $(NH_2BH_2)_x$, are left.[17] Thus, the diammoniate reacts somewhat as if it were a mixture of ammonium hydroborate and aminoborane (Structure V). In fact, when the diammoniate is treated with excess trimethyl amine, the products are exactly what would be expected on this basis: hydrogen, ammonia, trimethylamine-borane, and aminoborane.

$$B_2H_6 \cdot 2\,NH_3 + (CH_3)_3N \longrightarrow NH_3 + H_2 + (CH_3)_3N:BH_3 + {}^1/_3(NH_2BH_2)_3. \quad (5.6)$$

Vapor pressure studies in liquid ammonia have shown that the remaining

[13] S. G. Shore and R. W. Parry, *J. Am. Chem. Soc.*, **80**, 8 (1958).

[14] E. Wiberg, *Ber.*, **69B**, 2816 (1936).

[15] H. I. Schlesinger and A. B. Burg, *J. Am. Chem. Soc.*, **60**, 290 (1938).

[16] W. L. Jolly, University of California Radiation Laboratory Report No. 4504, May, 1955.

[17] G. W. Schaeffer, M. D. Adams, and F. J. Koenig, *J. Am. Chem. Soc.*, **78**, 725 (1956).

aminoborane is trimeric, and reactions with sodium show the trimer to be a monobasic acid:[18]

$$N_3B_3H_{12} + Na \longrightarrow Na^+ + N_3B_3H_{11}^- + \frac{1}{2} H_2. \qquad (5.7)$$

Thus, the evolution of 1.33 equivalents of hydrogen in the reaction of the diammoniate with excess sodium is explained.

Parry[19] has proposed Structures VIA and VIB, in which the cations are B^{3+} ions complexed by hydride ions and ammonia molecules. Direct evidence for the $H_2B(NH_3)_2^+$ cation was obtained in the reactions of ammonium halides with the diammoniate:[20]

$$[H_2B(NH_3)_2]BH_4 + 2 NH_4X \longrightarrow 2[H_2B(NH_3)_2]X + 2 H_2. \qquad (5.8)$$

Structure VIA is presumed to represent the species in fresh, cold ammonia solutions; the reaction with sodium is explained as follows:

$$(H_3N:BH_2:NH_3)BH_4 + Na \longrightarrow NaBH_4 + \frac{1}{x} (BH_2NH_2)_x + \frac{1}{2} H_2 + NH_3. \qquad (5.9)$$

Structure VIA is thought to rearrange to Structure VIB, which reacts with sodium as follows:

$$HB(NH_3)_3(BH_4)_2 + 2 Na \longrightarrow 2 NaBH_4 + HB(NH_2)_2 + H_2 + NH_3. \qquad (5.10)$$

It will be noted that Structures III, V, and VIA are tautomers; they differ simply in the positions of the hydrogen atoms. Chemical data will probably never decide the exact structure of solid diborane diammoniate; it will be necessary to use some technique such as neutron diffraction or nuclear magnetic resonance.

POLYARYL CHROMIUM COMPOUNDS

Hein and his coworkers[21] prepared an extensive series of polyaryl chromium compounds starting with the crude product obtained from the reaction of phenyl magnesium bromide with chromium(III) chloride. The scheme for preparing some of the more important members of the series is outlined in Figure 5.2. The structures proposed by Hein for these compounds are given in the first column of Figure 5.3. These structures are unreasonable for at least two reasons. First, the magnetic susceptibilities of all the compounds

[18] H. Hornig, W. Jolly, and G. Schaeffer, Paper presented at Miami A.C.S. Meeting, April, 1957, Division of Inorganic Chemistry.

[19] R. W. Parry and S. G. Shore, *J. Am. Chem. Soc.*, **80**, 15 (1958).

[20] D. R. Schultz and R. W. Parry, *J. Am. Chem. Soc.*, **80**, 4 (1958).

[21] See F. A. Cotton, *Chem. Revs.*, **55**, 551 (1955).

FIGURE 5.2

The Preparation of Aromatic Chromium Compounds

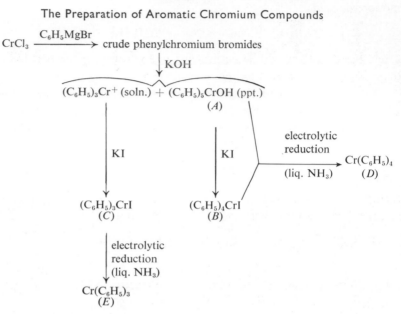

correspond to the presence of one free electron per chromium.[22] Second, when one mole of compound B is reduced with lithium hydroaluminate, two moles of biphenyl (and no benzene) is formed.[23] These observations may be accounted for by the structures (due to Klemm and Neuber[22]) given in the second column of Figure 5.3, where each chromium is in the $+5$ oxidation state.

However, phenyl magnesium bromide is recognized as a reducing agent but not as an oxidizing agent. Thus it is difficult to account for the formation of tetra-, penta-, and hexavalent chromium compounds. One would also expect that hydrogen atoms which are directly bonded to chromium atoms (as in the Klemm and Neuber structures) would be hydridic in character; however, these compounds are quite stable in aqueous solution. In addition, when compound B is reduced with lithium deuteroaluminate, the biphenyl produced contains only 5D per cent instead of the 10D per cent expected from the Klemm and Neuber structure. A similar reduction of compound C gives biphenyl containing 6.7D per cent instead of 10D per cent. Zeiss and Tsutsui[23] have explained these data in terms of the sandwich structures given in the third column of Figure 5.3. Presumably, when a deuteride ion attacks

---

[22] W. Klemm and A. Neuber, *Z. anorg. Chem.*, **227**, 261 (1936).

[23] H. Zeiss and M. Tsutsui, *J. Am. Chem. Soc.*, **79**, 3062 (1957). (In this reference L. Onsager is credited with proposing the structures in the third column of Figure 5.3.)

one of the four phenyl groups of compound B (*bis*biphenylchromium(I) iodide), the entire complex collapses with expulsion of a non-deuterated biphenyl molecule and the formation of one monodeuterobiphenyl molecule

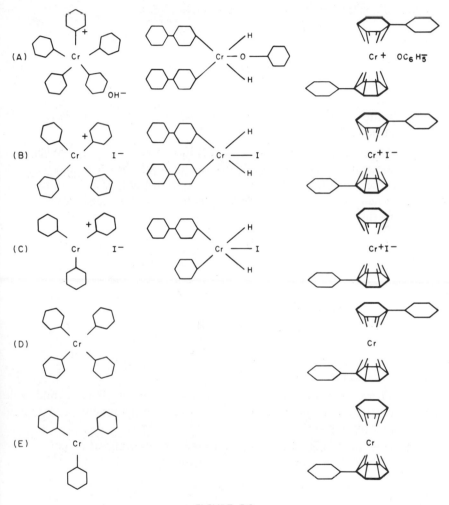

FIGURE 5.3.
Proposed structures for the aromatic chromium compounds.

and evolution of hydrogen. Indiscriminate deuteride reduction at either benzene or biphenyl sites in compound C (benzenebiphenylchromium(I) iodide) would explain the 6.7D per cent in this case.

It will be noted that the sandwich structures are analogous to the structure of ferrocene (*bis*cyclopentadienyliron(II)). In *bis*arenechromium(0), the chromium accepts twelve π-electrons to attain a krypton configuration, and in ferrocene, the iron accepts ten π-electrons to attain a krypton configuration. It has been suggested that nickel may form a sandwich complex with cyclobutadiene, where the nickel accepts eight π-electrons.[24]

PROBLEMS

1. One of the products of the pyrolysis of beryllium diethyl is a white solid. When this solid is treated with excess water, both methane and hydrogen are evolved in the ratio $CH_4/H_2 = 1/4$. Presuming the white solid to be a pure compound, what can be said about its structure?

2. There exist two isomers (A and B) of dimethyl diborane. When one mole of isomer A is hydrolyzed, one mole of boric acid and one-half mole of *bis*(dimethylboryl)oxide, $(CH_3)_2BOB(CH_3)_2$, are formed. When one mole of isomer B is hydrolyzed, two-thirds mole of trimethylboroxin is formed:

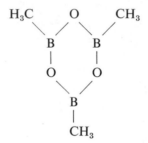

   What is the structure of each isomer?

3. There exist four isomers of dimethylborazine. How would you partially distinguish them by the amounts of hydrogen evolved upon hydrolysis?

4. How might one decide between the two following structures for the pyrosulfite ion on the basis of chemical evidence?

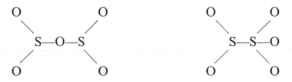

5. A sodium polyphosphate solution is passed through a cation-exchange resin column in the hydrogen form (thus converting all the sodium ions to protons). The resulting solution is titrated with

[24] H. Longuet-Higgins and L. E. Orgel, *J. Chem. Soc.*, 1969 (1956).

0.1 M NaOH. Two endpoints are found (at pH 4 and 9), at 42 ml. and 50 ml. Assuming that the polyphosphate consists of linear chains, what is the average number of phosphorus atoms per chain?

6. The equilibrium constant for the dissociation of a chloride ion from $AgCl_{(aq)}$ is much smaller than that for the dissociation of a chloride ion from $AgCl_2^-$.

$$AgCl_{(aq)} = Ag^+ + Cl^- \qquad K = 4.9 \times 10^{-4}$$
$$AgCl_2^- = AgCl_{(aq)} + Cl^- \qquad K = 1.2 \times 10^{-2}.$$

May we conclude that the two chlorine atoms in $AgCl_2^-$ are structurally different?

CHAPTER 6

GENERAL LABORATORY PROCEDURES

Course Prerequisites

You should be familiar with the elementary techniques of analytical chemistry and organic chemistry (weighing, precipitation, filtration, crystallization, desiccation, distillation, extraction, titration, and melting-point determination). If you feel the need for reviewing any of these topics, you may wish to consult one or more of the following texts:

I. M. Kolthoff and E. B. Sandell, "Textbook of Quantitative Inorganic Analysis," 3rd ed., Macmillan, New York, 1952.

A. R. Olson, C. W. Koch, and G. C. Pimentel, "Introductory Quantitative Chemistry," Freeman, San Francisco, Calif., 1956.

R. E. Dodd and P. L. Robinson, "Experimental Inorganic Chemistry," Elsevier, New York, 1954.

R. Adams and J. R. Johnson, "Elementary Laboratory Experiments in Organic Chemistry," 4th ed., Macmillan, New York, 1949.

J. Cason and H. Rapoport, "Laboratory Text in Organic Chemistry," Prentice-Hall, Englewood Cliffs, N. J., 1950.

A. I. Vogel, "Elementary Practical Organic Chemistry. Part I. Small Scale Preparations," Longmans, Green and Co., New York, 1957.

Outline of Laboratory Work[1]

After you have received your locker assignment, your first job is to check carefully the contents of the locker against the list of locker equipment given in Appendix 9. Any items which are missing may be obtained from the store-room. During the remainder of the first laboratory period, you are to prepare a sample of copper(I) chloride, following the directions given on page 142. Starting with the next laboratory period, and continuing for about eleven weeks, you will be expected to complete several assignments. These are described below.

FIVE REQUIRED SYNTHESES

Between the first laboratory period and the last three weeks of the semester, you will be expected to prepare five compounds of your own choice. You will be somewhat restricted in your choice of compounds. First, each preparation must be approved by the instructor. (The instructor will disallow preparations which are trivial, too difficult, or too dangerous.) Second, each of the synthesized compounds must be of a different "type." An arbitrary list of "compound types" is given in Table 6.1. Third, during the semester

TABLE 6.1

Some Types of Compounds

Type	Examples
Strong Oxidizing Agent	K_2FeO_4, KO_2, $K_2S_2O_8$
Strong Reducing Agent	$NaNH_2$, $Cr(OAc)_2$, NH_2OH
Complex Compound	$K_2Ni(CN)_4 \cdot H_2O$, $[Co(NH_3)_5Cl]Cl_2$
Organo-metallic Compound	$Pb(C_6H_5)_4$, LiC_6H_5, $Fe(C_5H_5)_2$
Volatile Halide	$VOCl_3$, SO_2Cl_2, BBr_3
Polymer	$(NaPO_3)_x$, $(PNCl_2)_x$, $(BH_2NH_2)_x$
Volatile Hydride	PH_3, B_2H_6, N_2H_4
Gas (miscellaneous)	N_2O, CO, $(CN)_2$
Metal	Cd plate, Si (thermite), Ge (H_2 reduction)
Intermetallic Compound	Na_4Pb_9, $NaSn_2$, Ca_3As_2
"Sub"-Compound	Ag_2F, Cs_7O_2, Na_xWO_3
Miscellaneous Compound	Li_3N, S_4N_4, $HOPO(NH_2)_2$

at least five of the "special techniques" listed in Table 6.2 must be used.

[1] Some instructors will consider the directions given in this chapter too detailed for use in their own classes, and will wish to modify the directions extensively. Perhaps these instructors will find some useful teaching ideas in the directions. (See the third paragraph of the Preface.)

TABLE 6.2

Some Special Techniques

1. Electrolytic oxidation or reduction.
2. Use of high-temperature process involving controlled atmosphere.
3. Use of high-temperature process not involving controlled atmosphere.
4. Use of non-aqueous solvent.
5. Vacuum manipulation.
6. Use of inert-atmosphere box.
7. Use of electric discharge.
8. Use of ion-exchange column.
9. Use of high-pressure apparatus.
10. Fractional or continuous extraction.

These techniques are described in Chapters 7–15. Lists of supplementary references and references to syntheses involving particular techniques are in these chapters.

Ordinarily, you will not be furnished with directions for the preparation of any of the compounds prepared after the first day. Rather you will devise synthetic methods based on your knowledge of the chemistry involved and on information obtained from the literature. Advantage should be taken of any appropriate synthetic procedures described in the literature, but you will be expected to attempt improvement of the existing methods with respect to one or more of the following points:

1. Simplicity of procedure,
2. Purity of product,
3. Percentage yield of product,
4. Cost of product.

The purity of the five products must be evaluated by quantitative or semi-quantitative analyses. In many cases, sharpness of melting point or boiling point will be acceptable criteria of purity. In other cases, qualitative analyses for the more likely impurities may suffice. In cases in which simple criteria such as the foregoing are impossible, a quantitative analysis (preferably volumetric) may be necessary. The following standardized solutions will be available:

$$0.1 \ N \ NaOH,$$
$$0.1 \ N \ HCl,$$
$$0.1 \ N \ Na_2S_2O_3,$$
$$0.1 \ N \ KMnO_4.$$

VACUUM-LINE ANALYSIS

During one laboratory period, you must perform an analysis using the vacuum line. You may choose either to determine the equivalent weight of an acid in liquid ammonia or to analyze a mixture of volatile materials. (See pp. 103–108.) Notify your instructor of your choice as soon as possible, and he will reserve the vacuum line for you for a particular date.

"SYNTHETIC TOURNAMENTS"

One or two "synthetic tournaments" will be held during the semester. In these tournaments each student will attempt to make a particular compound as quickly as possible, with as high yield as possible, and with the greatest possible purity. About two weeks before each tournament, the instructor will announce the compound to be prepared and the weight of starting material which is to be provided. The following syntheses have been found to be satisfactory for a three-hour laboratory period:

The conversion of 10 grams of potassium dichromate to chromium(II) acetate.

The conversion of 5 grams of lead dioxide to ammonium hexachloro-plumbate(IV).

The conversion of 10 grams of granulated tin to ammonium hexachloro-stannate(IV).

The conversion of 10 grams of potassium permanganate to potassium manganate(VI).

The conversion of 5 grams of potassium nitrite to $K_4[ON(SO_3)_2]_2$. (This compound must be kept at $0°$ in order to prevent its decomposition.)

GLASS-BLOWING ASSIGNMENT

As soon as possible, you should attain sufficient glass-blowing skill so that you can satisfactorily perform the following operations:

1. Make a closed round end on a tube,
2. Join, in a straight line, two tubes of unequal bore,
3. Make a "T" connection.

Directions for these operations are given in Appendix 1, and your instructor will demonstrate these operations. However, no amount of reading or instruction can replace actual practice with a torch if any dexterity is sought. Several torches will be available for use by the class, and you are advised to spend your spare laboratory time practicing glass blowing.

SPECIAL RESEARCH PROBLEM

During the last three weeks of the semester, you will work on a minor research problem which will involve the preparation of some entirely new compound or will involve a new synthetic method for a known compound. Around the middle of the semester, a list of research problems will be posted from which you may choose a problem. The results of this research will be written up in the style of a typical article from the Journal of the American Chemical Society.

You should examine a recent copy of the Journal of the American Chemical Society in order to acquaint yourself with the general style and arrangement of the articles. It will be noted that each article is prefaced by a brief abstract which summarizes the main points. The main body of the article is usually divided into three or more parts, for example:

Introduction	or	Introduction
Experimental, and		Experimental
Discussion		Results, and
		Discussion

References should be numbered in one consecutive series and abbreviations for titles of journals should conform to those used by *Chemical Abstracts*. Periodical references should be punctuated as in the following examples.

J. C. Bailar, Jr., *J. Chem. Education*, **34**, 334 (1957).

T. Moeller and D. H. Wilkins, *Inorg. Syntheses*, **4**, 101 (1953).

Book references are punctuated as in the following examples (which you may wish to consult).

E. J. Crane, A. M. Patterson, and E. B. Marr, "A Guide to the Literature of Chemistry," John Wiley and Sons, New York, 1957.

S. F. Trelease, "The Scientific Paper. How to Prepare It. How to Write It," The Williams and Wilkins Co., Baltimore, Md., 1947.

Laboratory Notebook

A bound notebook, approximately 8″ × 10″, should be used. Before proceeding with any preparation, notes from the literature, the expected main and side reactions, the physical properties of the reactants and products, and yield calculations are written in the notebook. At this time the notebook is shown to the instructor; he may ask questions concerning the experiment and may make certain suggestions regarding the procedure.

During the course of a preparation, all significant observations should be recorded immediately. Drawings should be made of apparatus. At the conclusion of a preparation, the notebook and the prepared compound should be given to the instructor.

Safety in the Laboratory

No laboratory work will be permitted in the absence of the instructor or teaching assistant except with written approval of the instructor.

Safety goggles must be worn whenever you are in the laboratory.

Familiarize yourself with the location and the use of the first-aid cabinet and the fire extinguishers. Volatile solvents should be handled in the hood.

Typical Laboratory Schedule

Table 6.3 gives a hypothetical week-by-week schedule for one student. A fifteen-week semester with two three-hour laboratory periods per week has been assumed.

TABLE 6.3

A Hypothetical Schedule

Week	Laboratory Work
1st	Checking of locker; preparation of CuCl
1st, 2nd, 3rd	Preparation of $CrCl_3$ ("volatile" halide and high-temperature process involving controlled atmosphere)
3rd	Glass blowing
4th	Preparation of $[Cr(NH_3)_5Cl]Cl_2$ (coordination compound and use of inorganic non-aqueous solvent)
5th	Vacuum-line analysis (identification of O_2, H_2O, and $CHCl_3$ in an "unknown" mixture)
6th, 7th, 8th	Separation of rare earths ("miscellaneous" compounds and use of ion-exchange column)
9th, 10th	Preparation and analysis of AgO (strong oxidizing agent and use of electrolytic apparatus and vacuum line)
10th	Synthetic tournament (preparation of $Cr(OAc)_2$)
11th, 12th	Preparation of $HOPO(NH_2)_2$ ("miscellaneous" compound)
13th, 14th, 15th	Special Research Problem: The preparation of H_2S_2.
15th	Checking of locker

CHAPTER 7

Electrolytic

SYNTHESES

The theoretical yield of an electrolytic process can be readily calculated from the current (I) and the time (t) for which it flows.

$$\text{Theoretical Yield} = \frac{(\text{Equivalent wt. of product}){\cdot}I{\cdot}t}{96,500},$$

where I is measured in amperes and t in seconds. In practice, yields fall below the theoretical value because of competing side reactions which cause formation of unwanted by-products. The "percentage yield," or *current efficiency* of an electrolytic process is given by the relation

$$\text{Current Efficiency} = \frac{\text{Yield}}{\text{Theoretical Yield}}{\cdot}100.$$

Since electricity is sold in terms of watt-hrs., not ampere-hrs., a quantity of more commercial significance is the *energy efficiency*, or yield per kilowatt-hour.

$$\text{Yield per kwh.} = \frac{\text{Yield}{\cdot}1000}{\text{Voltage}{\cdot}\text{Amperage}{\cdot}\text{Hours}}.$$

Current efficiency may be increased by reducing the extent of the side reactions. The yield per kilowatt-hour may be increased by increasing the

74

current efficiency and by decreasing the voltage. Of course the applied voltage cannot be decreased below the thermodynamically required value (the reversible potential); in fact, for the reasons discussed below, the applied potential is almost always appreciably greater than the reversible potential.

THE CURRENT-VOLTAGE CURVE

The electrical properties of an electrolytic cell are much different from those of a simple ohmic resistance. In general, the current varies with the applied voltage as curve C of Figure 7.1. Practically no current flows even when the

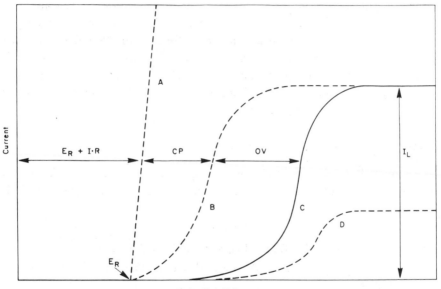

FIGURE 7.1.

A typical electrolytic current-voltage curve (E_R is the reversible cell potential, $I \cdot R$ is the product of the current and the cell resistance, CP is the concentration polarization, OV is the overvoltage, and I_L is the limiting current).

applied voltage equals the reversible cell potential, E_R. If the electrode processes were completely reversible, increasing the potential beyond this point would cause the current to rise along line A, whose slope equals the reciprocal of the cell resistance. But actually, opposing potentials (whose magnitudes increase with increasing current) are established in the cell, and these prevent the current from increasing without bound.

Since ions are either formed or removed at the electrode surfaces, concentration gradients are built up in the vicinity of the electrodes. These concentration gradients cause a potential drop called *concentration polarization*. (Curve *B*, Figure 7.1, is the current-voltage curve for a cell with concentration polarization.) At sufficiently high currents, the concentration of reacting species (the depolarizer) becomes practically zero at an electrode surface. Then the current becomes independent of the applied voltage and is controlled only by diffusion and migration of the ions and by stirring the electrolyte. If the solution is well stirred and contains a high concentration of inert electrolyte, the value of the limiting current is directly proportional to the concentration of the reacting species.

Curve *D* represents the current-voltage curve which would be observed if the concentration of depolarizer were reduced by a factor of one-third.

An electrode reaction, like any chemical reaction, possesses an activation energy. This activation energy appears in the form of an overvoltage (labeled *OV* in Figure 7.1). Some electrode reactions, such as metal electrodepositions, have very low or practically no overvoltages; others, such as those involving gas evolution, have high overvoltages. Overvoltage is briefly discussed in the following sections.

HYDROGEN AND OXYGEN OVERVOLTAGES

If a potential greater than 1.23 volts is applied to inert electrodes immersed in an aqueous solution of some "inert" electrolyte (such as H_2SO_4, NaOH,

TABLE 7.1

Hydrogen Overvoltages in 1 M H_2SO_4 in Volts[1]

Cathode	Current Density in Amperes per Square Centimeter		
	10^{-2}	10^{-1}	1
Pt (black)	0.03	0.04	0.05
Pt (smooth)	0.07	0.29	0.68
Au	0.39	0.59	0.80
Fe	0.56	0.82	1.29
Cu	0.58	0.80	1.25
C	0.70	0.89	1.17
Ni	0.74	1.05	1.24
Zn	0.75	1.06	1.23
Ag	0.76	0.98	1.10
Al	0.83	1.00	1.29
Hg	0.93	1.03	1.07
Pb	1.09	1.18	1.26
Cd	1.13	1.22	1.25

[1] W. M. Latimer, "Oxidation Potentials," 2nd ed., Prentice-Hall, Englewood Cliffs, N. J., 1952.

or Na_2HPO_4), the decomposition of water into hydrogen and oxygen is thermodynamically possible. But even when concentration polarization effects are minimized, it is usually found that potentials much greater than 1.23 volts must be applied before appreciable gas evolution occurs. These potentials are required because the overvoltages for evolution of hydrogen and oxygen are very high at most electrodes.

Tables 7.1 and 7.2 give hydrogen and oxygen overvoltages, respectively, for various electrode surfaces. It may be noted that mercury, lead, and cadmium exhibit extremely high hydrogen overvoltages and that platinum and gold exhibit high oxygen overvoltages. Since overvoltage is markedly affected by the condition of the electrode surface, the values are only approximate.

TABLE 7.2

Oxygen Overvoltages in I M KOH in Volts[1]

Cathode	Current Density in Amperes per Square Centimeter		
	10^{-2}	10^{-1}	1
Ni	0.35	0.73	0.87
Pt (black)	0.40	0.64	0.79
Cu	0.42	0.66	0.84
C	0.52	1.09	1.24
Ag	0.58	0.98	1.14
Au	0.67	1.24	1.68
Pt (smooth)	0.72	1.28	1.38

Most cathodic and anodic processes in aqueous solution are accompanied by the evolution of hydrogen and oxygen, respectively. There are various ways whereby the ratio of hydrogen to desired cathode product or the ratio of oxygen to desired anode product may be decreased: (1) One may use an electrode possessing a high overvoltage for hydrogen or oxygen evolution; (2) One may apply a voltage such that the ratio of hydrogen or oxygen to desired product is minimized; (3) The concentration of the species which leads to the desired product may be increased; (4) The temperature may be decreased. (Since hydrogen and oxygen overvoltages are higher than most other overvoltages, a given decrease in temperature will usually cause a greater decrease in the rate of formation of hydrogen or oxygen than in the rate of formation of the desired product.)

Methods (1) and (2) may be used to increase the current efficiency of the reduction of chromic ion to chromous ion in acidic solution. (See Figure 7.2.) The thermodynamically favored cathode process is the reduction of hydrogen ion; it may be made the exclusive process if a "platinized" platinum electrode

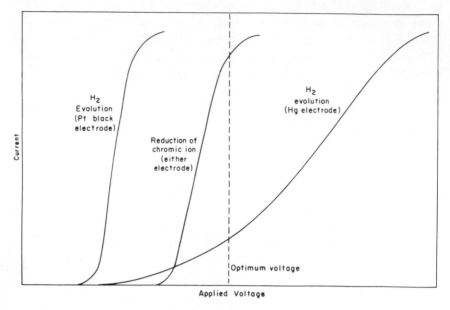

FIGURE 7.2.
Reduction of hydrogen ion and chromic ion.

is used. But if a mercury cathode is used at the appropriate current density, the chromic ion reduction is the important process. The application of methods (3) and (4) to the decrease of oxygen evolution is discussed later in this chapter under Effect of Concentration and Effect of Temperature.

EFFECT OF THE ELECTRODE MATERIAL

Some electrolytic processes have overvoltages comparable in magnitude to hydrogen and oxygen overvoltages. The cathodic reduction of nitric acid is an interesting case in which changes in the cathode material profoundly influence the course of the reaction. Table 7.3 gives the current efficiencies for the production of hydroxylammonium ion and ammonium ion at various cathodes. In all cases, the current density was 0.24 amp./cm^2.

Catalysts are often added to an electrolyte to change the current efficiency at an electrode. For example, salts of mercury, lead, or cadmium are often added to increase the hydrogen overvoltage at a cathode. Salts of titanium, vanadium, chromium, iron, or cerium are sometimes added to an electrolyte when the metal ions are capable of undergoing oxidation-reduction reactions both at the electrode and with the depolarizer.

TABLE 7.3

Current Efficiencies in Reduction of Nitric Acid[2]

(0.4 g. HNO_3 in 20 ml. 50 per cent H_2SO_4; cooled with ice)

Cathode	NH_3OH^+ *per cent*	NH_4^+ *per cent*
Amalg. lead	69.7	16.9
Smooth zinc	45.8	38.3
Rough lead	26.8	57.6
Smooth copper	11.5	76.8
Spongy copper	1.5	93.8

The literature abounds with data on electrolytic catalysts; in many cases the mechanisms of the catalysts are unknown.

EFFECT OF THE ELECTRODE POTENTIAL

There are often several processes which can occur at an electrode. If these several processes have current-potential curves (*cf.* Figure 7.3) which are well

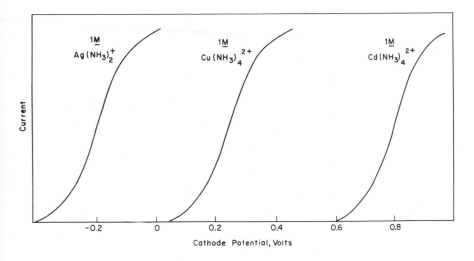

FIGURE 7.3.

Electroplating current-voltage curves.

separated, it is possible, by careful control of the applied electrode potential, to carry out one process to the exclusion of the others. The method of *electrolysis with controlled cathode potential* is used quite commonly in the

[2] J. Tafel, *Z. anorg. Chem.*, **31**, 289 (1902).

analysis of solutions containing several kinds of metal ions. For example, a solution containing $Ag(NH_3)_2^+$, $Cu(NH_3)_4^{2+}$ and $Cd(NH_3)_4^{2+}$, with standard oxidation potentials -0.37, $+0.06$ and $+0.61$ volt, respectively, can first be electrolyzed with a cathode potential of -0.15 volt until practically all the silver has been plated out, then the copper may be plated out at a potential of $+0.4$ volt, and, finally, the cadmium is plated out at potentials greater than $+0.61$ volt.

The reduction of an alcoholic solution of nitrobenzene at a platinum cathode furnishes an example in which the reducible substance may be reduced to either of two substances, depending on the cathode potential. With a cathode potential of 0.6 volt, the principal product is azoxybenzene; with a cathode potential of 1.0 volt, the principal product is hydrazobenzene.[3]

An electrode potential cannot be readily calculated from the over-all applied voltage; it must be measured with the aid of a suitable reference anode

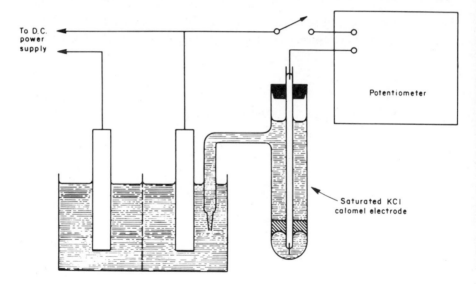

FIGURE 7.4.
Apparatus for measuring electrode potentials.

at essentially zero current flow. The simple apparatus pictured in Figure 7.4 is adequate for measuring an electrode potential during an electrolysis.

It is important to realize that, even though the applied voltage is held constant during an electrolysis, the potential of the electrode at which the important reaction is taking place will not remain constant. If we assume, for

[3] Haber, *Z. Elektrochem.*, **4**, 506 (1898).

simplicity, that the potential of the opposing electrode remains constant, we have the relation:

$$E_{electrode} + I \cdot R = \text{applied voltage} + \text{constant.}$$

After the electrolysis has proceeded a finite amount, the concentration of depolarizer will have decreased, causing a decrease in the current, I. The decrease in the I·R drop will result in a corresponding increase in the electrode potential. In order to hold the electrode potential constant, it is necessary to decrease continually the applied voltage throughout the electrolysis.

EFFECT OF CONCENTRATION

Consider an electrode at which several competing reactions are taking place. A change in the electrolyte composition can change the relative rates of the electrode reactions, and hence change their current efficiencies. For example, when a cold solution of sulfuric acid is electrolyzed with platinum electrodes, three anodic processes occur:

$$2 H_2O = O_2 + 4 H^+ + 4 e^-$$
$$2 SO_4^{2-} = S_2O_8^{2-} + 2 e^-$$
$$3 H_2O = O_3 + 6 H^+ + 6 e^-.$$

At 0°, the formation of oxygen and peroxydisulfate are the only important processes. From Table 7.4 we see that the relative production of oxygen and peroxydisulfate is quite sensitive to the concentration of sulfuric acid.

TABLE 7.4

Oxidation of Sulfuric Acid to Peroxydisulfuric Acid[4]

(Temp.: 0°;   Anode: Pt)

Sp. Gr. of H_2SO_4	Current Efficiency, per cent Current Density, amp./cm.[2]		
	0.05	0.5	1.0
1.15			7.0
1.20		4.4	20.9
1.25		29.3	43.5
1.30	1.8	47.2	51.6
1.35	3.9	60.5	71.3
1.40	23.0	67.7	75.6
1.45	32.9	73.1	78.4
1.50	52.0	74.5	71.8
1.55	59.6	66.7	65.3
1.60	60.1	63.8	50.8
1.65	55.8	52.0	
1.70	40.0		

[4] K. Elbs and O. Schönherr, Z. Elektrochem., **1**, 417 (1894).

In the electrodeposition of metals, changes in the composition of the electrolyte often cause changes in the character of the deposit. For example, if silver is plated out from a silver nitrate solution, the deposit is usually non-adherent and composed of large crystals. However, if the electrolyte contains excess cyanide (the silver being complexed as $Ag(CN)_2^-$), the deposit is firm and smooth.

EFFECT OF TEMPERATURE

Increasing the temperature of the electrolyte reduces the resistance of the cell and increases the rate of diffusion of the depolarizer. For these reasons, the energy efficiency is increased. Electrode reactions, just like ordinary reactions, have activation energies. Hence, if more than one reaction is occurring at an electrode, a change in the temperature of the electrode usually changes the relative rates of the electrode reactions. We have already seen (Table 7.4) how the yield of peroxydisulfate in the electrolysis of aqueous sulfuric acid is affected by changes of concentration at 0°. In Table 7.5, data are presented which show the effect of temperature on the production of ozone by the electrolysis of sulfuric acid of specific gravity 1.200 with a platinum anode.

TABLE 7.5

Ozone by Electrolysis of Sulfuric Acid[5]

Approx. Anode Temp. °C.	*Current Density* (amp./cm.²)	*Current Efficiency* per cent
0	0.29	0.78
	0.73	1.11
	2.93	1.27
−63	0.25	23.6
	0.75	32.4
	1.24	27.5

ELECTROLYSIS APPARATUS

Some laboratories are wired with direct current from a dynamo. Such direct-current power is usually supplied at 110 volts, and for most electrolyses it is necessary to reduce the voltage with a rheostat. When such a power supply is not available, one may rectify the ordinary 60-cycle alternating current. A simple apparatus such as that used for charging storage batteries

[5] J. D. Seader and C. W. Tobias, *Ind. Eng. Chem.*, **44**, 2207 (1952).

is satisfactory if direct current with a great deal of "ripple" is not detrimental to the electrolysis. However, when a steady direct current whose voltage is readily controlled is desired, an apparatus such as that diagrammed in Figure 7.5 is useful. This apparatus produces D.C. current with very little "ripple"; the applied voltage may be varied from 0 to 100 volts, and currents up to 8 amperes may be drawn.

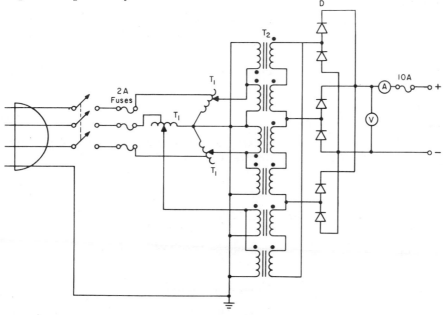

FIGURE 7.5.

A D.C. power supply.

T_1 1.5 amp variable transformers (ganged)
T_2 Selenium rectifier power transformers (Stancor RT–202)
D Sarkes-Tarzian 10–LF silicon diodes
V 0–100 v. voltmeter
A 0–10 a. ammeter

When setting up an electrolytic cell, make certain that the wires leading to the electrodes are well insulated. Do not connect the power plug until your set-up has been checked by the instructor.

ELECTROLYTIC SYNTHESES

The following electrolytic preparations are listed simply as examples of preparations you might perform in the laboratory. You are not restricted to these examples; rather you are encouraged to try other syntheses.

Compound	Reference
$K_2S_2O_8$ $KClO_2$ $KClO_4$ $TiCl_3 \cdot 6\,H_2O$ $KMnO_4$	H. F. Walton, "Inorganic Preparations," Prentice-Hall, Englewood Cliffs, N. J., 1948.
$BaFeO_4 \cdot H_2O$ $PbCrO_4$	W. E. Henderson and W. C. Fernelius, "Inorganic Preparations," McGraw-Hill Book Co., New York, 1935.
$Co_2(SO_4)_3 \cdot 18\,H_2O$	*Inorg. Syntheses*, **5**, 181 (1957).
$Co_2(SO_4)_3 \cdot 18\,H_2O$ $(NH_4)Co(SO_4)_2 \cdot 12\,H_2O$ $(NH_4)V(SO_4)_2 \cdot 12\,H_2O$ $(NH_4)_2MoCl_5 \cdot H_2O$ $(NH_4)_3Mo(SCN)_6 \cdot 4\,H_2O$ $KClO_3$ $KClO_4$ $KBrO_3$	W. G. Palmer, "Experimental Inorganic Chemistry," Cambridge University Press, 1954.
Barium or strontium amalgam	*Inorg. Syntheses*, **1**, 11 (1939).
NH_2OH	Schtscherbakow and Libina, *Z. Elektrochem.*, **35**, 826 (1929).
$Agpy_4(NO_3)_2$	Barbieri, *Ber.*, **60**, 2424 (1927).
$Ag_7O_8NO_3$ AgO	Noyes, DeVault, Coryell, and Deahl, *J. Am. Chem. Soc.*, **59**, 1326 (1937).
$CrSO_4 \cdot 5\,H_2O$	S. Glasstone and A. Hickling, "Electrolytic Oxidation and Reduction," Chapman and Hall, London, 1935, pp. 122–123.
$K_3Mn(CN)_4$	Grube and Brause, *Ber.* **60**, 2273 (1927).
$Na_2S_2O_4 \cdot 2\,H_2O$	Glasstone and Hickling, pp. 240–244.
$Na_2S_4O_6$	Glasstone and Hickling, pp. 247–253.
$Na_2S_2O_6$	Glasstone and Hickling, pp. 253–258.
$AsH_{0.25}$	Jolly, Anderson, and Beltrami, *J. Am. Chem. Soc.*, **79**, 2443 (1957).
Rare earth amalgams (from alcohol)	*Inorg. Syntheses*, **1**, 15 (1939).
Lithium (from acetone)	Patterson and Mott, *J. Phys. Chem.*, **12**, 65 (1908).
NR_4 amalgams (from alcohol)	McCoy and Moore, *J. Am. Chem. Soc.*, **33**, 273 (1911).

Pb(OAc)$_4$ (from HOAc)	Schall and Melzer, *Z. Elektrochem.*, **28**, 474 (1922).
Cd, Cr, Co, Cu, Au, In, Fe, Pb, Ni, Pt metals, Ag, Sn, Zn	A. G. Gray, Ed., "Modern Electroplating," The Electrochemical Society, Inc., John Wiley and Sons, New York, 1953.
Na, Sr, Cd, Sn, Sb, Bi, As (from acetone)	Mott, *Trans. Electrochem. Soc.*, **15**, 529 (1909).
Ag$_2$F	A. Hettich, *Z. anorg. allgem. Chem.*, **167**, 67 (1927).
K$_3$W$_2$Cl$_9$	*Inorg. Syntheses*, **5**, 139 (1957).
H$_2$NC(NH)N$_2$H$_3$	Shreve and Carter, *Ind. Eng. Chem.*, **36**, 423 (1944).
K$_3$[MoCl$_6$]; K$_2$[MoCl$_5$H$_2$O]	*Inorg. Syntheses*, **4**, 97 (1953).
Electrodeposition from non-aqueous solvents	Audrieth and Nelson, *Chem. Revs.*, **8**, 335 (1931).
Practically all metals	T. M. Rodgers, "Handbook of Practical Electroplating," Macmillan, New York, 1959.

PROBLEMS

1. Potassium chlorate was prepared by the electrolytic oxidation of potassium chloride. A current of 1 ampere was passed for 2 hours. Assuming a current efficiency of 50 per cent, how many grams of KClO$_3$ should have been obtained?

2. If germane may be prepared by the cathodic reduction of aqueous H$_2$GeO$_3$ with a current efficiency of 2 per cent, how long would it take to prepare 5 millimoles of germane with a current of 2 amperes?

3. Explain why it is possible to reduce the sodium ion at a mercury cathode even though the reduction of water to hydrogen is the thermodynamically favored process. How would you expect changes in pH and temperature to affect the current efficiency?

CHAPTER 8

HIGH-TEMPERATURE PROCESSES

THERMOCOUPLES

Two wires of different metals joined at their ends to form a loop constitute a thermocouple. If the two junctions are at the same temperature, no current will flow through the loop. However, if the junctions are at different temperatures, there will usually be a current flow. If the circuit is broken and a potentiometer is connected across the break, one may measure an electromotive force which depends only on the metals used and the temperatures of the junctions. Thus thermocouples may be used as temperature-measuring devices having definite advantages over the usual liquid-in-glass thermometers. They are less liable to breakage and have a much wider temperature range.

Thermocouples made of Chromel P (90% Ni, 10% Cr) and Alumel (98% Ni, 2% Al) wire are commonly used; these thermocouples may be used at temperatures as high as 1100°C. For accurate work, it is necessary that each thermocouple be calibrated by measuring the electromotive force corresponding to various temperatures. However, for most synthetic purposes it is adequate to use the approximate data in Table 8.1, which gives the electromotive force as a function of the hot-junction temperature when the cold junction is held in an ice-water bath. Whenever it is unnecessary to know high temperatures to better than $\pm 5°$, one may dispense with the

ice-water bath and simply allow the cold junction to remain at room temperature. The data of Table 8.1 may still be used in such cases if the observed
voltages are increased by one millivolt. In fact, it is most convenient to

TABLE 8.I

Chromel-Alumel Thermocouple

(Fixed Junction 0°)

°C.	0°	20°	40°	60°	80°
0°	0.00	0.82	1.65	2.48	3.32
100°	4.15	4.98	5.79	6.59	7.39
200°	8.19	9.00	9.82	10.64	11.46
300°	12.29	13.12	13.96	14.79	15.63
400°	16.48	17.33	18.18	19.03	19.88
500°	20.74	21.59	22.44	23.30	24.15
600°	25.00	25.85	26.69	27.55	28.37
700°	29.21	30.03	30.85	31.66	32.47
800°	33.28	34.08	34.88	35.66	36.46
900°	37.25	38.04	38.82	39.60	40.37

simply interpose the potentiometer between the two dissimilar metal wires
(see Figure 8.1). Some potentiometers, such as Leeds and Northrup's Model
8657, have devices for compensating for a cold junction which is at room
temperature instead of 0°C. With such compensation, the potentiometer
readings may be used without correction.

When rather crude temperature measurement (± 20°C.) will suffice, a
simple high-resistance millivoltmeter may be used instead of a potentiometer.
Such meters usually give slightly low temperature readings because of the
finite I·R drop through the thermocouple.

Care must be taken to prevent shorting the thermocouple wires. If the
wires are allowed to touch at a place other than the hot junction, a spurious
reading will be obtained, since the voltage will correspond to the temperature
of the colder junction. Thermocouple wires are generally insulated and protected by a double-bore ceramic sheath for a distance of about one foot from
the point at which the wires are welded together. When it is necessary to
make the sheath airtight or when it is necessary to protect the thermocouple

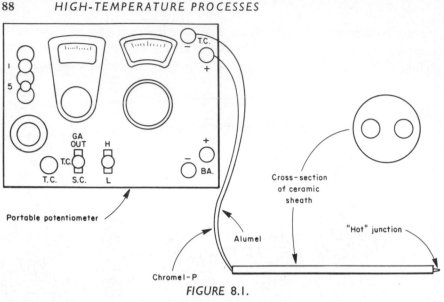

FIGURE 8.1.

Simple thermocouple circuit.

wires from chemical attack, a glass, ceramic, or metal tube (closed at one end) may be slipped over the ceramic sheath.

RESISTANCE FURNACES

There are three main types of electric furnaces available for studying high-temperature reactions: muffle furnaces, "pot" furnaces, and tube furnaces. Muffle furnaces are simply high-temperature ovens; they are primarily for heating materials in crucibles without a controlled atmosphere. Muffle furnaces are usually provided with their own temperature-controlling mechanisms and thermocouple pyrometers. Pot and tube furnaces are usually used for heating materials in controlled atmospheres. Typical set-ups for these types of furnaces are pictured in Figure 8.2. These furnaces usually do not have their own temperature-regulating mechanisms; it is customary to control their power input (and consequently their temperature) with auto-transformers.

It must be remembered that, while a reaction vessel is being warmed up in a pot furnace or tube furnace, the outer surface of the vessel may be several hundred degrees warmer than the interior of the vessel. Thus one might easily melt a glass reaction vessel during a warm-up if one naïvely relied upon the readings of a thermocouple placed inside the vessel. Precautions must also be taken when the thermocouple is placed outside the reaction vessel. The thermocouple must not be placed too close to the heating ele-

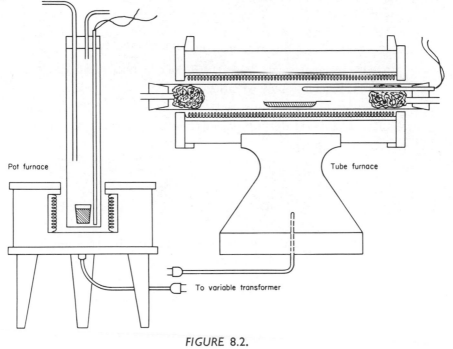

FIGURE 8.2.
A "pot" furnace and tube furnace.

ments, or the temperature reading will be higher than that inside the reaction vessel, even after the warm-up period.

CHOOSING CONTAINERS

Consider the following laboratory mishaps:

1. An iron crucible was ruined when a student used it as a reaction vessel for the dehydration of NaH_2PO_4 to $(NaPO_3)_x$. A platinum or porcelain crucible should have been used.

2. A platinum boat was ruined when a student melted aluminum in it. A graphite container would have been satisfactory, since the fusion was carried out in a nitrogen atmosphere.

3. A quartz tube was ruined when a student heated magnesium in direct contact with it. The magnesium should have been contained in an alumina boat.

4. Numerous platinum dishes have been ruined because they were used for alkaline fusions. In most cases porcelain or iron dishes could have been used.

Your allowed breakage fee is not infinite, and chemical equipment is very expensive. So for the sake of both your pocketbook and your reputation as a chemist, think carefully before you carry out any high-temperature reaction. Consider the following questions:

1. Are the reactants acidic? If so, will the container be affected?
2. Will the reactants alloy with the container?
3. Is the reactant a strong reducing agent? If so will the container be affected? (Strong oxidizing agents should be considered similarly.)
4. Will the oxygen of the air react with the container?

BIBLIOGRAPHY

R. E. Dodd and P. L. Robinson, "Experimental Inorganic Chemistry," Elsevier, New York, 1954, pp. 69–72.

American Institute of Physics, "Temperature; Its Measurement and Control in Science and Industry," Reinhold Pub. Corp., New York, 1941, vol. I. (See also vol. II, 1955.)

P. H. Dike, "Thermoelectric Thermometry," Leeds and Northrup Co., Philadelphia, 1954.

C. Duval, "Inorganic Thermogravimetric Analysis," Elsevier, New York, 1953.

For choosing a container for a molten metal:

R. N. Lyon, Ed., "Liquid Metals Handbook," 2nd ed. (rev.), Office of Naval Research, 1954.

CHAPTER 9

THE INERT ATMOSPHERE BOX

The Inert Atmosphere Box

Non-volatile, air-sensitive materials are conveniently handled in an inert atmosphere box (or, less precisely, a "dry box"). If the materials to be handled are only sensitive to the water or carbon dioxide in the air, the box may be filled with air which has been freed of these gases. If oxygen-sensitive materials are to be handled, the box may be filled with nitrogen. However, some materials, such as lithium, are reactive even toward nitrogen, and require a box filled with an inert gas such as argon.

Many types of dry boxes have been described in the literature.[1] Figure 9.1 is a schematic sketch of an evacuatable argon box. Instructions for using this box are given in the following paragraphs.

Make sure that the inner door is clamped shut and that valve D is closed. If the lock is at atmospheric pressure, the outer door may now be opened. However, if the lock is evacuated, it must first be brought to atmospheric pressure by admitting argon through valve B (valve A open; valve C closed). (DANGER! Do not permit the pressure in the lock to exceed atmospheric pressure.) Put the materials in the lock (remove the tops from all bottles), close and clamp the outer door, and evacuate the lock to a pressure of about 50 microns by opening valve C. Now close valve C and admit argon to a pressure of about 1/10 atmosphere. Reevacuate and finally fill the lock with

[1] S. Y. Tyree, Jr., *J. Chem. Education*, **31**, 603 (1954); T. R. P. Gibb, Jr., *Anal. Chem.*, **29**, 584 (1957); R. E. Johnson, *J. Chem. Education*, **34**, 80 (1957).

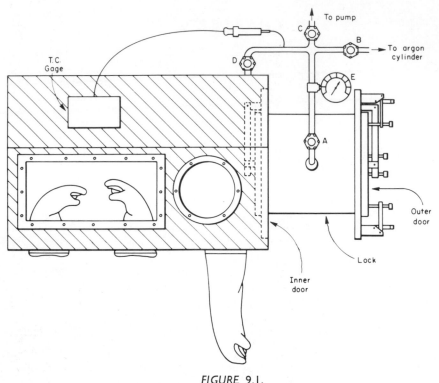

FIGURE 9.1.
Inert atmosphere box.

one atmosphere of argon. The inner door may now be opened and the materials transferred from the lock to the dry box. When you have finished working in the dry box, put the materials back in the lock and clamp the inner door shut. The outer door may now be opened and the materials may be taken from the lock.

Never take volatile materials into the dry box. Keep the interior of the box clean. It is often useful to take a large piece of aluminium foil into the box and to carry out operations which might involve scattering crystals, and so on, over the aluminum foil. When you are finished working, the debris can be wrapped up in the foil and conveniently removed through the lock.

Apply liberal amounts of talcum powder to the hands and gloves before working in the box. It is helpful to wear an auxiliary pair of tight-fitting rubber gloves in order to keep the main gloves free from perspiration. If you find a hole in a glove, report immediately to your instructor.

The Inert Atmosphere Bag

When simple operations with small apparatus must be performed in an inert atmosphere, it is sometimes convenient to use a transparent polyethylene bag. The apparatus is placed in the bag, the bag is flushed with argon and sealed. It is then possible to handle materials within the bag by grasping them from the outside. A thin polyethylene bag offers very little impediment to manipulation and is practically impervious to moisture.

CHAPTER 10

THE VACUUM LINE

GENERAL DESCRIPTION OF THE VACUUM LINE

The main parts of the vacuum line you will use in this course are schematically pictured in Figure 10.1. It will be noted that the traps are lettered (*A* to *D*) and the stopcocks are numbered (1 to 14). These letter and number designations will be useful in later discussions. Several parts of the vacuum system not shown in Figure 10.1 are described in some detail in the following pages. It is suggested that you prepare yourself for using the vacuum line not only by studying these pages, but also by examining the vacuum line first-hand in the laboratory. You may wish to consult Sanderson, "Vacuum Manipulation of Volatile Compounds," or Dodd and Robinson, "Experimental Inorganic Chemistry," Chapter 2. Bring any questions you may have to your instructor.

GROUND JOINTS

The most reliable method for joining a glass apparatus to a glass vacuum system is to make a fused seal (see Appendix 1). However, when the connection must be made and broken frequently, and when the materials being handled are unreactive toward grease, it is much more convenient to use a ground joint. There are two main types of ground joints—conical joints and ball-and-socket joints; these are illustrated in Figure 10.2. Conical joints are used whenever bending at the joint cannot be tolerated. However,

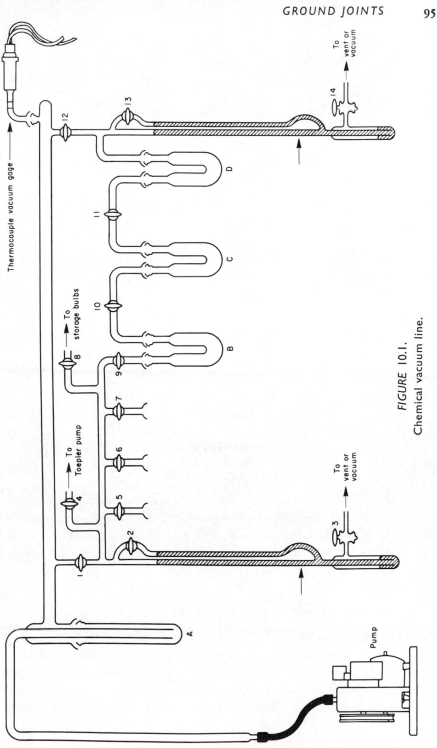

FIGURE 10.1.

Chemical vacuum line.

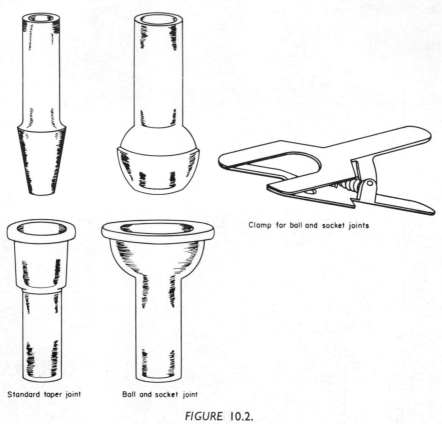

Clamp for ball and socket joints

Standard taper joint   Ball and socket joint

FIGURE 10.2.
Ground joints.

the flexibility of the ball-and-socket joint is generally an advantage, and the latter joints are more popular on vacuum lines. Both types of joints must be sealed with grease in order to render them gas-tight. Ball-and-socket joints must be clamped together, which can best be accomplished with spring clamps such as the one illustrated in Figure 10.2.

STOPCOCKS AND MERCURY FLOAT VALVES

The commonest types of stopcock used in high-vacuum work are illustrated in Figure 10.3. Both types have provision for evacuation of the small bulb behind the plug. When properly lubricated and evacuated, such stopcocks will not pop open at pressures as high as two atmospheres.

There are many vapors which dissolve in, or react with, the usual type of

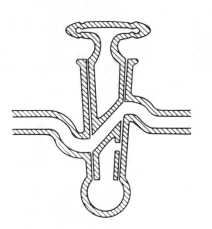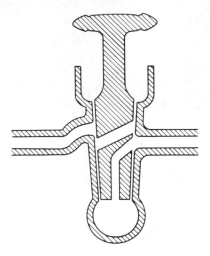

FIGURE 10.3.
High-vacuum stopcocks.

stopcock grease. It is often possible to avoid serious contamination of stop-cock grease by such vapors by keeping the vapor pressures low and by expos-ing the vapors to the stopcock grease for only short periods of time. When these precautions are inconvenient, one may replace ordinary greased stop-cocks with mercury float valves.

A mercury float valve (see Figure 10.4) consists of a small U-tube con-nected between the parts of the apparatus to be closed from each other. Each arm of the U-tube contains a glass float with a ground joint in the arm. When the valve is open, the floats rest on glass supports formed by indenting the tube. The valve is closed by admitting mercury from the reservoir into the U-tube, where it forces the floats into place. The ground joints do not permit leakage of mercury under pressure differentials of one atmosphere or less.

On the present vacuum line, mercury float valves are used to connect the main system with storage vessels containing purified organic solvents such as diethyl ether, "diglyme," and so on.

MEASURING VAPOR PRESSURES AND VAPOR VOLUMES

The mercury-filled bubbler-manometers which are located at each end of the vacuum line serve dual purposes. Ordinarily, the two cocks of a bubbler-manometer are open. Then the device serves both as a pressure-relief valve

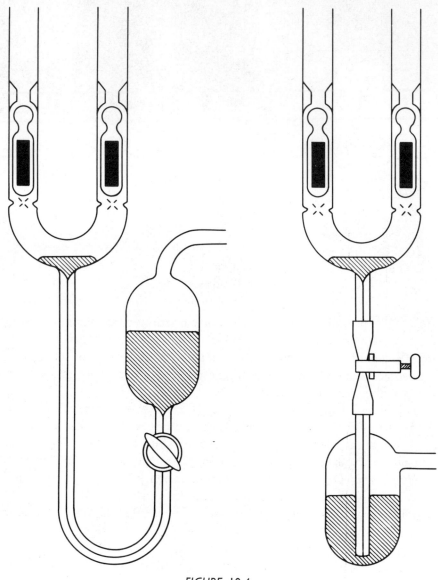

FIGURE 10.4.
Mercury float valves.

and as a crude manometer. However, it is occasionally desired to employ the device as an accurate, "constant-volume" manometer. In order to make the device ready for such service, the system is evacuated and the upper cock is closed. Then an increase in pressure in the system will cause the mercury in the left tube of the manometer to be depressed; the mercury in the right tube will remain at approximately the same level. The difference in the heights of the menisci may be read with either a rule or a cathetometer. When you wish to know the volume of a gas whose pressure is being measured, it is necessary that the left meniscus be brought to a reproducible level (marked with an arrow on Figure 10.1). The mercury level may be adjusted by applying a vacuum through the lower cock. Great care must be taken that the left meniscus is never allowed to go down as far as the connection to the right tube of the manometer, or mercury will be thrown up against the upper closed cock with such violence that the apparatus will break.

The volumes of the four isolable sections of the vacuum line (the sections between cocks 1 and 9, cocks 9 and 10, cocks 10 and 11, and cocks 11 and 12) should be known. Then it is possible to measure a gas with either bubbler-manometer and in any of several possible volumes. When convenient, a bulb or tube of known volume may be connected below cock 5, 6, or 7 so that large or small volumes of gas may be measured.

Let us imagine that there is some carbon dioxide in trap *B*, and that you wish to determine its purity and its amount. Attach a small ampoule of known volume below cock 5 and open cock 5. Then thoroughly evacuate the system to the left of trap *B* through cock 1. Close cocks 1 and 2, and open cock 9. (From the observed pressure and a knowledge of the volumes of the various parts of the system, you may quickly calculate whether or not the gas can be contained in the system to the left of trap *B*. We shall assume that this is possible.) Condense all the sample into the ampoule with liquid nitrogen and close cock 9. Then remove the liquid nitrogen from around the ampoule and allow it to warm to room temperature. Close cock 3 and connect the house vacuum to the tube leading from cock 3. By careful manipulation of cock 3, adjust the level of the left meniscus to the "zero" mark. Then read the pressure and the room temperature. With these data and the known volume of the system, you may now calculate the number of millimoles of vapor present, assuming perfect gas behavior.

Let us say you wish to know something about the purity of the carbon dioxide. One useful criterion of purity is the constancy of vapor pressure with vapor volume. Immerse the ampoule in a CS_2-slush (see Appendix 2). The vapor pressure of pure CO_2 at the temperature of melting carbon disulfide is 26 mm. If the measured vapor pressure is greater than 26 mm., the sample is probably contaminated with a volatile substance. Momentarily open cock 9. After reaching equilibrium if the vapor pressure is now lower, you can be sure that such a contaminant is present. If you immerse trap *B* in liquid

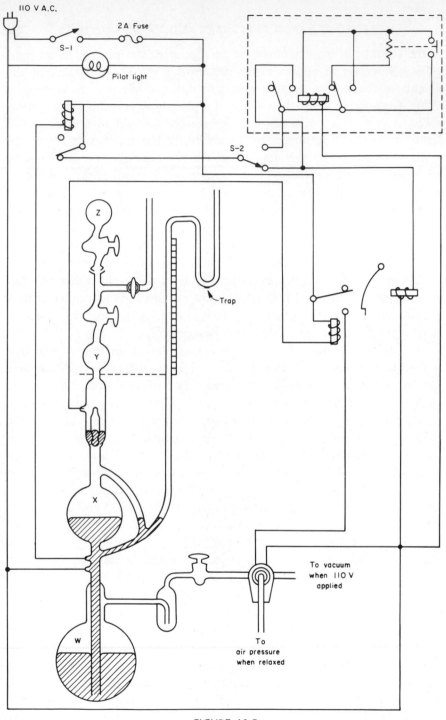

FIGURE 10.5.
Toepler pump with automatic control.

nitrogen and repeat the above operation several times, you will effect a crude fractional distillation of the sample. If the last portions of sample remaining in the ampoule have vapor pressures appreciably less than 26 mm., the sample is contaminated with some material less volatile than CO_2.

It should be noted that constancy of vapor pressure with vapor volume is not an absolute proof of purity. Other measurements (such as melting point determination, chemical analysis, and so forth) should be made, if possible, to supplement vapor-pressure measurements.

OPERATION OF TOEPLER PUMP

The Toepler pump shown in Figure 10.5 is used for pumping "non-condensible" gases (such as H_2 or N_2) from the main system into bulb Y. The pump contains almost enough mercury to fill the reservoir W. When in operation, air pressure forces the mercury up through chamber X and through the float valve, at which time a vacuum is applied to the reservoir and the mercury is pulled down into the reservoir again. This cycle is repeated enough times to force 99.9 per cent or more of the gas in the system through the float valve, where it is trapped in bulb Y. Switch S-1 is now opened and, by careful manipulation of the stopcock between the reservoir and the solenoid valve, the mercury level is brought to a mark on the tubing immediately below bulb Y. The pressure of the gas in bulb Y may now be read directly from the rule next to the inlet tube of the pump. If it is desired to transfer the gas to bulb Z (e.g., for a molecular-weight determination), the cock immediately above bulb Y is opened and the mercury is allowed to rise to a point just below the open cock of bulb Z. After closing this cock the mercury is lowered by closing switch S-1 and opening the stopcock between the reservoir and the solenoid valve. Always close the cock above bulb Y before removing bulb Z from the system.

When pumping relatively small amounts of gas, it is often desirable to turn switch S-2 to the upper position, thus actuating the time-delay circuit. Now the mercury will rise from the reservoir several seconds after being pumped down. Thus the gas has time to reach pressure equilibrium between cycles. This is an unnecessary refinement, however, and the control circuit can be considerably simplified by omitting the section within the dashed-line rectangle.

THERMOCOUPLE VACUUM GAGE

The thermocouple vacuum gage is based on the fact that the thermal conductivity of a rarified gas increases with increasing pressure. The gage consists of an electrically heated wire to which a thermocouple is attached. At a

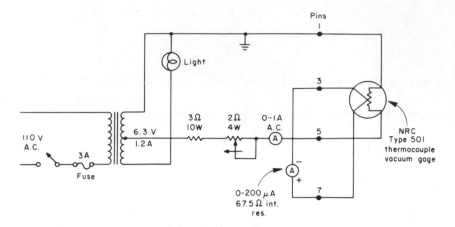

FIGURE 10.6.
Thermocouple gage circuit.

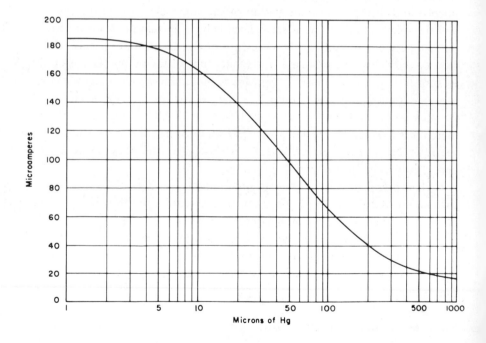

FIGURE 10.7.
Thermocouple gage calibration curve for air.

constant gas pressure, the wire and thermocouple quickly reach a steady-state temperature, at which point the rate of heat loss by gaseous conduction to the walls of the tube approximately equals the electrical heat input of the wire. The greater the heat conductivity of the gas, the lower will be the wire temperature. The thermal conductivity of a gas increases with increasing pressure and with decreasing molecular weight (if the molecular complexity is held constant).

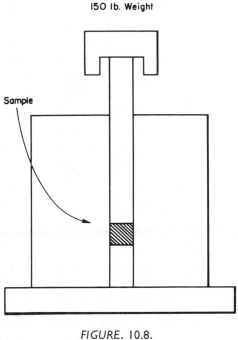

FIGURE. 10.8.
Pill press.

Figure 10.6 gives a diagram of the circuit associated with the gage, and Figure 10.7 gives a calibration curve (microamperes *vs.* pressure in microns) for dry air. It will be noted that the gage is of little use at pressures outside the range 1–500 microns. However, pressures lower than 1 micron are not obtainable with the present vacuum line.

EQUIVALENT WEIGHT OF UNKNOWN ACID[1]

Your instructor will give you a small amount of a crystalline compound which is a strong acid in liquid ammonia. You will determine the equivalent

---

[1] See Chapter 6 for a discussion of the required vacuum-line analysis.

weight of the acid by measuring the hydrogen evolved when the acid is allowed to react with excess sodium-ammonia solution. In the following directions, it is assumed that the vacuum line has been pumped down with all the cocks closed except cocks 1, 2, 3, 13, and 14.

The unknown acid will be in the form of non-hygroscopic crystals and will require no drying. Using the metal "pill-press" (see Figure 10.8), prepare a pellet of the acid weighing 80–100 mg. Weigh the pellet to ± 0.2 mg. and place it in the side-arm of the reaction vessel (see Figure 10.9). Cut a clean, pea-sized piece of sodium (*ca.* 0.1 g.) and put it in the bottom of the vessel. Grease the ball joint; connect it to the socket below cock 5, and evacuate the vessel by opening cock 5. This last operation should be performed quickly to minimize the reaction of air with the sodium.

Connect an ammonia cylinder to the socket below cock 6 with Tygon tubing, and open cock 6. When the pressure has decreased to about 30 microns, close cock 1 and *carefully* open the ammonia-cylinder valves (the main valve first) so that ammonia bubbles at a moderate rate through the mercury bubbler. Cool the reaction vessel with liquid nitrogen until about 5–10 cc. of solid ammonia has condensed in the vessel; then close the ammonia-cylinder valves, and then close cock 6. Open cock 1 until the pressure has decreased to about 10 microns; then close cock 1. Remove the liquid-nitrogen bath from the reaction vessel until ammonia begins bubbling through the mercury bubbler; then freeze the sodium-ammonia solution with liquid nitrogen and open cock 1 until the pressure has again reached about 10 microns.

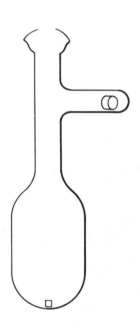

FIGURE 10.9.
Reaction vessel.

Remove the liquid nitrogen bath from the reaction vessel and wait until the vapor pressure of the ammonia reaches about 10 cm.; then immerse the vessel in a chloroform slush. (See Appendix 2.) Tip the reaction vessel slightly, and, by tapping, knock the acid sample into the sodium-ammonia solution. After about ten minutes, the reaction is complete and the vessel is again immersed in liquid nitrogen. The hydrogen may now be Toepler-pumped through a liquid-nitrogen trap (to remove the small amount of uncondensed ammonia) into bulb *Y*.

ANALYSIS OF VOLATILE MIXTURE[1]

The volatile unknown consists of a mixture of two or three substances, each of which has a vapor pressure greater than 5 mm. at room temperature. Your problem is to identify the components of the mixture and to determine their amounts. In the following direc-tions, it is assumed that the vacuum line has been pumped down with all the cocks closed except cocks 1, 2, 3, 13, and 14.

Separation. The components are separ-able by fractional condensation. This is a necessary restriction for a simple unknown mixture, because without any previous knowledge of the components, you would be hard put to devise a method (*e.g.*, a chemical method) for separating two closely boiling materials.

The sample will be contained in a glass vessel such as that pictured in Figure 10.10. Attach the sample tube to the tube-opener with Apiezon *W* wax and connect the tube-opener to the joint below cock 5. Open cock 5 and immerse the sample tube in liquid nitrogen. When the pressure in the system has decreased to about 10 microns, close cock 1 and break the fragile tip of the sample tube by turning the cock of the tube-opener. If the manometer indicates an increase in pressure, the sample contained some gas which is not completely con-densible with liquid nitrogen. Immerse the trap immediately above the Toepler pump (see Figure 10.5) in liquid nitrogen. Open cock 4 and Toepler-pump the gas into a tared bulb (bulb *Z*) of known volume, and measure the temperature and pressure of the gas.

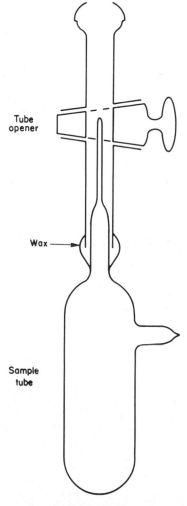

Tube opener

Wax →

Sample tube

FIGURE 10.10.
Sample tube and tube opener.

If the sample contained a non-conden-sible gas, the remaining condensible material may be a pure substance. Of course, if the remaining material exists as two liquid phases at room temperature, you can be sure that there are two condensible components. However, if only one phase remains, it is best to determine the vapor pressure as a function of vapor volume at some convenient temperature. If the material is thus shown to be a mixture, or if there was no non-condensible gas, follow some procedure such as that outlined below for separating the mixture.

If you can find the temperature at which the vapor pressure of the more volatile component of the mixture is 1–20 mm., and at which the vapor pressure of the less volatile component is "negligible" (for practical purposes, less than 10^{-2} mm.), then you can effect a good separation of the mixture by passing the vapors through a trap held at this temperature. It is best to seek this temperature in a system of small volume (so as to have a low vapor volume). A list of suitable cold baths is given in Appendix 2.

If the mixed vapors are passed through the cold trap too rapidly, the efficiency of the separation may suffer for two possible reasons. (1) The less volatile component may not be thoroughly condensed in the cold trap; it may be partially carried through the trap (entrained) by the more volatile component. Hence, the more volatile fraction may be contaminated with the less volatile component. (2) Since the pressure in the system is relatively high, the more volatile component may partially condense in the cold trap. Hence, the less volatile fraction may be contaminated by the more volatile component.

If the mixture is distilled too slowly some of the less volatile component may leave the cold trap by simple evaporation. (Even the less volatile component has a finite vapor pressure at the temperature of the trap). Hence, the more volatile fraction may be contaminated by the less volatile component.

As a rough rule, we may say that an efficient separation will be effected if the materials are distilled at a rate of approximately one millimole per minute. Some high-boiling liquids will distill from an ordinary 2-cm.-diameter reaction tube much slower than this. In fact, water will usually freeze and then sublime very slowly. In such cases it is wise to surround the tube with a bath of warm water. When distilling liquids whose boiling points are below 100°, the liquid is first frozen to a solid button in the bottom of the distillation tube. During the distillation, the tube is allowed to warm up gradually in the air. If the material boils below −50°, the same procedure is followed except that the distillation tube is immersed in an empty Dewar to reduce the rate of sublimation.

Figure 10.11 may be used to decide the proper trap temperature to use when separating two materials whose boiling points are known. For example, let us suppose we wish to separate a mixture of ether (b.p. = 34.6°) and stibine (b.p. ∼ −20°). Since Δ b.p. ∼ 55°, we see, from the graph, that a

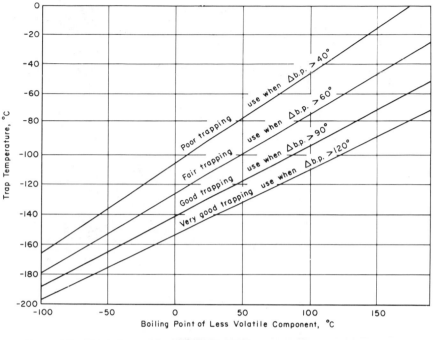

FIGURE 10.11.

Suggested cold-trap temperatures for separating volatile mixtures.

trap at approximately $-100°$ should be used to condense out the ether. A toluene slush $(-95°)$ would work very well. A carbon disulfide slush $(-111.6°)$ would probably trap out some stibine and would be usable only if the distillation were carried out very slowly.

An experiment performed by Schaeffer, Schaeffer, and Schlesinger[2] admirably illustrates the effectiveness of a simple fractionating train. A mixture of 82.3 cc. (S.T.P.) of borazole, $B_3N_3H_6$, and 23.8 cc. (S.T.P.) of boron trichloride was allowed to react at room temperature for 116 hours. The material remaining consisted of B-dichloroborazole, B-monochloro-borazole, unreacted borazole, diborane, and hydrogen. These materials were separated by pumping through four traps. A schematic flow-diagram is shown in Figure 10.12.

Identification of components. Your unknown mixture will not contain more than one "non-condensible" component. Therefore, a molecular-weight determination will be of considerable aid in identifying the material.

[2] G. W. Schaeffer, R. Schaeffer, and H. I. Schlesinger, *J. Am. Chem. Soc.*, **73**, 1612 (1951).

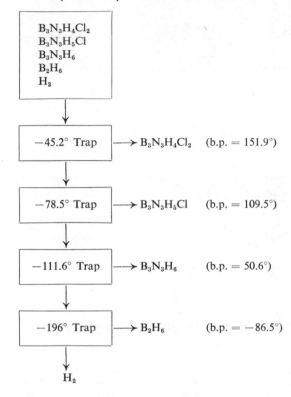

FIGURE 10.12

A Separation by Fractional Condensation

(Weigh bulb Z, which contains the non-condensible gas, so that the molecular weight may be calculated.) If, after determining the molecular weight, there is still ambiguity as to the identity of the material, various tests may be applied. For example, the vapor pressure at the temperature of liquid nitrogen may be measurable; or some simple chemical reaction may be carried out. Discuss the problem with your instructor and he will help you devise some method of identification.

Determine the vapor pressure of each condensible component at one or two of the following temperatures: $-111.6°$, $-78.5°$, $0°$, $20°$. If you assign reasonable limits of error to your measurements and assume (correctly) that the compound is listed in Sanderson,[3] then you should be able to reduce the possibilities to less than a half dozen compounds. A molecular weight determination or a simple chemical test should permit a final identification.

[3] R. T. Sanderson, "Vacuum Manipulation of Volatile Compounds," John Wiley and Sons, New York, 1948, pp. 123–149.

BIBLIOGRAPHY

R. T. Sanderson, "Vacuum Manipulation of Volatile Compounds," John Wiley and Sons, New York, 1948.

R. E. Dodd and P. L. Robinson, "Experimental Inorganic Chemistry," Elsevier, New York, 1954, Chapter 2.

A. Stock, "Hydrides of Boron and Silicon," Cornell University Press, 1933, Chapter 30.

S. Dushman, "Scientific Foundations of Vacuum Technique," John Wiley and Sons, New York, 1949.

A. Farkas and H. W. Melville, "Experimental Methods in Gas Reactions," Macmillan, New York, 1939.

PROBLEMS

Relating to "unknown acid" experiment:

1. Why is the main ammonia cylinder valve opened first?

2. Why is the freshly distilled ammonia allowed to melt and then refrozen before adding the acid sample?

3. What are the equivalent weights, in liquid ammonia, of

    a) ammonium bromide?
    b) phosphonium iodide?
    c) acetamide?
    d) phthalimide?
    e) sulfamic acid?

4. Exactly 11.2 cc. (S.T.P.) of a colorless material is found to weigh 23 milligrams. The vapor pressure at 0° is measured as 11 ± 1 mm. When this material is distilled onto excess sodium-ammonia solution and allowed to react, 5.8 cc. (S.T.P.) of hydrogen is evolved. What is the material?

5. Why would the following materials make poor "unknown" acids?

    a) ammonium nitrate
    b) ammonium sulfate.

Relating to "volatile unknown" experiment:

1. The molecular weight of a pure gas is determined to be 29 ± 1. What are the various possibilities and how would you uniquely identify each?

2. How would you separate (without destruction) a mixture of

   a) helium and argon?
   b) ammonia and water?
   c) hydrogen chloride and water?

3. How would you analyze a mixture of

   a) nitrogen and carbon monoxide?
   b) hydrogen and helium?
   c) methylamine and trimethylamine?

General:

1. How would you separate a mixture of GeH_4 (b.p. $-88°$), Ge_2H_6 (b.p. $30°$), and Ge_3H_8 (b.p. $111°$)?

2. A particular Toepler pump reduces the pressure in a system from P to $0.8P$ during each cycle of its operation. For how many cycles must the pump operate in order to remove 99.5 per cent of the gas in the system?

CHAPTER II

ELECTRICAL-DISCHARGE

TUBES

In a sufficiently high electrical field, a gas becomes conducting and an *electrical discharge* is established. The following processes may occur in an electrical discharge:

1. Elastic impacts between electrons (e^-) and molecules (M), where there is no great energy transfer.

2. Electron addition reactions in which negative ions are formed:

$$e^- + M \longrightarrow M^-.$$

3. Ionization impacts of the type:

$$e^-(\text{fast}) + M \longrightarrow M^+ + 2e^-(\text{slow}).$$

The positive ions may form clusters thus:

$$M^+ + M \longrightarrow M_2^+,$$

and neutralization of such a cluster releases energy which may serve as activation energy for a chemical reaction:

$$e^- + M_2^+ \longrightarrow \text{Products}.$$

4. Excitation impacts of the type:

$$e^-(\text{fast}) + M \longrightarrow M^* + e^-(\text{slow}).$$

The excited molecule may return to its normal state with emission of radiation,

$$M^* \longrightarrow M + h\nu,$$

or it may dissociate into free radicals or atoms. For example:

$$H_2(^3\Sigma_u^+) \longrightarrow 2\ H + \text{kinetic energy.}$$

Thus in an electrical discharge it is possible to have chemical reactions initiated by ions, excited and metastable molecules, radicals, and atoms. In many respects the situation is similar to that existing in systems exposed to high-energy radiation (gamma rays, X-rays, ultraviolet light, beta rays, and so on).

Various types of discharge tubes and the reactions which have been studied in them are discussed in a book by Glocker and Lind.[1] Another book, by Steacie,[2] contains a valuable section on methods for the production and detection of atoms and radicals. Two types of discharge tubes are used in this course: the Siemens ozonizer and the microwave discharge tube.

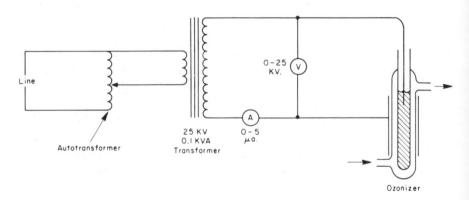

FIGURE 11.1.
Ozonizer circuit.

THE OZONIZER

A schematic diagram of the ozonizer and its power supply is given in Figure 11.1. It will be noted that the ozonizer looks much like a condenser with one end closed off. (In fact, a condenser may serve as a convenient substitute for an ozonizer.) The inner and outer cylinders are separated by about 5 mm.;

[1] G. Glocker and S. C. Lind, "The Electrochemistry of Gases and Other Dielectrics," John Wiley and Sons, New York, 1939.

[2] E. W. R. Steacie, "Atomic and Free Radical Reactions," 2nd ed., Reinhold Publ. Corp., New York, 1954, pp. 32-70.

when in operation, 10–25 kv. (60 cycle) is applied across the gap. One electrical contact is made to a salt solution in the inner "finger"; the other is made to aluminium foil wrapped around the outer cylinder.

Changes in the following variables have been found to influence the yields of reactions carried out in ozonizers:

1. Applied voltage
2. Frequency of current
3. Gap distance
4. Flow rate of gases
5. Pressure of gases
6. Material of which ozonizer constructed
7. Temperature.

DANGER: The operation of the ozonizer is extremely hazardous because of the possibility of electrocution and, in some cases, of explosion. Never make any electrical connections to the ozonizer except under the direct supervision of the instructor. The ozonizer may be operated only in the presence of the instructor.

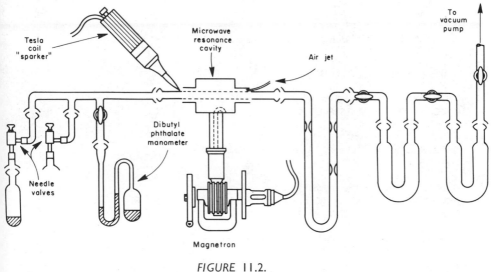

FIGURE 11.2.
Microwave discharge apparatus.

THE MICROWAVE DISCHARGE

The microwave energy is generated in a continuous-wave magnetron oscillator tube which is powered by a full-wave rectifier unit, fully filtered, using separ-

ate plate and filament transformers.[3] The input to the high voltage trans-
former is controlled by a variable auto-transformer which provides for control of the output of the magnetron tube. The power output is indicated on a
milliammeter. The radiation passes through a coaxial cable to a resonance
cavity, through which a glass tube containing the gas to be excited passes.[4]
It should be pointed out that a microwave discharge can be maintained in a
gas only at relatively low pressures (generally less than 5 mm. pressure).
A schematic diagram of the microwave generator and the associated vacuum
line is given in Figure 11.2.

REFERENCES TO DISCHARGE SYNTHESES

Discharge tubes, as used in the preparation of particular compounds, are
discussed in the following references:

E. B. Maxted, "Modern Advances in Inorganic Chemistry," Oxford University Press, 1947.	Atomic hydrogen and oxygen Active nitrogen Hydroxyl F_2O_2, ClO_2, Br_3O_8, BrO_2, I_4O_9, $NO_3(?)$, $P_2O_6(?)$, SO_4
T. P. Whaley, *J. Chem. Education*, **34**, 94 (1957).	O_3
Jolly, Anderson, and Beltrami, *J. Am. Chem. Soc.*, **79**, 2443 (1957).	As_2H_4
Inorg. Syntheses, **3**, 78 (1950).	N_2O_5
D. Meschi and R. Myers, *J. Am. Chem. Soc.*, **78**, 6220 (1956); A. V. Jones, *J. Chem. Phys.*, **18**, 1263 (1950).	S_2O
Pflugmacher and Dahmen, *Z. anorg. Chem.*, **290**, 184 (1957).	$(SiCl_3)_3N$
Urry, Wartik, Moore, and Schlesinger, *J. Am. Chem. Soc.*, **76**, 5293 (1954); J. W. Frazer and R. T. Holzmann, *J. Am. Chem. Soc.*, **80**, 2907 (1958).	B_2Cl_4
W. V. Kotlensky and R. Schaeffer, *J. Am. Chem. Soc.*, **80**, 4517 (1958).	B_6H_{10}, B_9H_{15}

[3] Commercial diathermy units are useful laboratory microwave generators. The units
manufactured by Baird Associates, Inc. (Cambridge, Mass.) and by Raytheon Manufac-
turing Co. (Waltham, Mass.) operate at a wavelength of 12.2 centimeters with a power
output of 125 watts.
[4] The design of microwave resonance cavities is discussed by E. C. Pollard and J. M.
Sturtevant, "Microwaves and Radar Electronics," John Wiley and Sons, New York, 1948,
pp. 44–54; and by M. Zelikoff, P. H. Wyckoff, L. M. Aschenbrand, and R. S. Loomis,
J. Opt. Soc. Am., **42**, 818 (1952).

A. Besson and L. Fournier, *Compt. rend.*, **150**, 102 (1910).   } P_2Cl_4

H. J. Schumacher and G. Sprenger, *Z. anorg. Chem.*, **182**, 139 (1929).   } NO_2Cl

M. Hogg and J. Spice, *J. Chem. Soc.*, **1958**, 4196. $(CS)_x$

A. Koenig and T. Brings, *Z. phys. Chem., Bodenstein Festband*, 541 (1931).   } N_2H_4

D. Shriver and W. Jolly, *J. Am. Chem. Soc.*, **80**, 6692 (1958).   } Ge_2Cl_6

U. Wannagat and G. Mennicken, *Z. anorg. allgem. Chem.*, **268**, 69 (1952).   } S_2O_7

W. C. Schumb, E. L. Gamble, and M. D. Banus, *J. Am. Chem. Soc.*, **71**, 3225 (1949).   } B_2I_4

A. Pflugmacher and W. Diener, *Angew. Chem.*, **69**, 777 (1957).   } B_2Br_4

CHAPTER 12

Non-aqueous
SOLVENTS

There are several reasons why it is often desirable to carry out reactions in a solvent:

1. In a solvent one may achieve intimate contact between reactants which otherwise would not react.

2. Reactions which are violent in the absence of a solvent may be carried out at a controlled rate in a solvent.

3. It may be possible to separate the product from by-products by utilizing solubility differences.

4. Many reagents are more conveniently handled when in solution than when in the pure state.

5. It is easier to measure out a certain *volume* of solution than to measure out a certain *weight* of material.

Water is the most commonly used solvent because it is cheap, it is readily available in high purity, and it dissolves many compounds. Unfortunately, many chemists behave as if water were the only usable solvent. Reactions which for one reason or another cannot be carried out in water are too often abandoned completely. This devotion to water is not caused so much by an unawareness of the existence of non-aqueous solvents as by an ignorance of the methods of handling them. It is hoped that you will learn some of these methods both in your own syntheses and by observing your fellow students.

TABLE 12.1
Some Protonic Solvents

Solvent	m.p., °C	b.p., °C	Dielectric Constant	Elect. Cond. mhos/cm.	$-\log K_{ion}$ 25°	$\Delta S_{vap.}$	$1000\ \eta$	$T_{b.p.}/V$
HF	−83.1	19.9	60 (19°)	1.4×10^{-5} (−15°)		6.1	2.4 (6°)	14.4
H_2SO_4	10.35	330	>84 (20°)	1×10^{-2} (20°)	3.4 (10°)		191 (25°)	11.3
HNO_3	−41.6	86		8.9×10^{-3} (0°)	~1.7 (−40°)		8.9 (20°)	8.6
HOOCH	8.3	100.5	47.9 (18.5°)	6×10^{-5}	~6	14.2	17.8 (20°)	9.9
HOAc	16.6	118.2	6.4 (20°)	5×10^{-9} (25°)	12.6	14.9	12.2 (20°)	6.8
HCN	−13.2	25.7	106.8 (25°)	5×10^{-7} (0°)	~18.7 (12°)	20.2	2.0 (20°)	7.7
H_2S	−85.5	−60.3	10.2 (−60°)	3.7×10^{-11} (−78°)		21.0	4.3 (−60°)	5.4
H_2O_2	−0.9	151.4	93.7	2×10^{-6} (25°)	13	27.3		17.9
H_2O	0.0	100.0	78.5 (25°)	4×10^{-8} (18°)	14.0	26.0	10.1 (20°)	20.7
CH_3OH	−97.9	64.7	31.5 (25°)		16.6	25.0	5.9 (20°)	8.3
C_2H_5OH	−114.6	78.5	24.2 (25°)		18.9	26.2	11.9 (20°)	6.0
N_2H_4	1.5	113.5	51.7 (25°)	2.3×10^{-6} (25°)	24.7	25.9	9.0 (25°)	12.2
NH_3	−77.7	−33.38	16.9 (25°)	1×10^{-11} (−33°)	27	23.3	2.5 (−33°)	9.6

TABLE 12.2
Some Aprotic Solvents

Solvent	m.p., °C	b.p., °C	D	Elect. Cond. mhos/cm.	1000 η	$T_{b.p.}/V$
SO_2	−72.7	−10.2	12.3 (22°)	4×10^{-8} (−10°)	4.28 (−10°)	5.9
$NOCl$	−61.5	−6.5	18.2 (12°)	2.9×10^{-6} (−20°)		5.8
$COCl_2$	−128	8.2	4.3 (22°)	7×10^{-9} (25°)		
N_2O_4	−11.3	21.1	2.4 (18°)	1.3×10^{-12} (17°)		9.3
$(C_2H_5)_2O$	−116.3	34.6	4.3 (20°)		2.22 (25°)	2.9
CS_2	−111.6	46.3	2.65 (20°)		3.76 (20°)	5.3
AsF_3	−8.5	63		2.3×10^{-5} (25°)		6.8
$n-C_6H_{14}$	−94	69	1.87 (20°)		3.26 (20°)	2.6
$SOCl_2$	−104.5	75.7	9.0 (22°)	1×10^{-8} (20°)		4.8
CCl_4	−22.9	76.8	2.24 (20°)		9.58 (21.2°)	3.6
C_6H_6	5.5	80.1	2.28 (20°)		6.47 (20°)	4.0
CH_3CN	−41	81.6	36 (20°)	5×10^{-8} (25°)	3.45 (25°)	6.8
$CH_3OCH_2CH_2OCH_3$	−69	85.2			11 (20°)	3.4
IF_5	9.6	98		1.6×10^{-5} (9.6°)		5.8
ICl	27.2	~98		4.4×10^{-3} (27°)		7.3
$POCl_3$	1.25	105.8	13.9 (22°)	1.7×10^{-6} (25°)		4.1
C_5H_5N	−40.7	115.5	12.5 (20°)	5.3×10^{-8} (18°)	9.45 (20°)	4.8
IBr	42	~116		4.0×10^{-4} (42°)		

TABLE 12.2 (continued)
Some Aprotic Solvents

Solvent	m.p. °C	b.p., °C	D	Elect. Cond. mhos/cm.	$1000\,\eta$	$T_{b.p.}/V$
BrF_3	8.8	127.6		8.1×10^{-3} (8.8°)		
$AsCl_3$	−18	130.2	12.8 (20°)	1.4×10^{-7} (0°)		4.8
$(CH_3)_2NCHO$	−61	153.0	37.6 (20°)			5.5
$CH_3O(CH_2CH_2O)_2CH_3$	−64	162.0			20 (20°)	3.1
$SeOCl_2$	10.9	176	46 (20°)	2×10^{-5} (25°)		
I_2	113.6	184.3	13.0 (168°)	1.7×10^{-4} (140°)		
$HgBr_2$	238	320	9.8	1.5×10^{-4} (242°)		

Physical properties. Tables 12.1 and 12.2 list the important physical properties of some non-aqueous solvents.

In general, substances which are not liquid at room temperature are impractical solvents. Thus I_2, IBr, and $HgBr_2$ (whose melting points are above room temperature) are of only academic interest as solvents. On the other hand, the cheapness and unique solubility properties of NH_3 and SO_2 more than compensate for the fact that these substances boil well below room temperature. And, although sodium hydrogen sulfate is a solid at room temperature, its melts are very useful for dissolving various refractory ores.

In general, a low viscosity is a desirable property in a solvent. In solvents with low viscosities, transfer operations such as pouring and filtering are rapid, precipitates are easily freed of solvent, and reactions which are diffusion-limited proceed rapidly. Thus the high viscosity of sulfuric acid is its major adverse property. Both dissolution and crystallization are very slow in this solvent.

SOLUBILITY OF NONELECTROLYTES

Hildebrand[1] has shown how various liquids may be characterized in terms of their internal pressures. (The internal pressure of a liquid is the molar energy of vaporization divided by the molar volume.)

The more nearly equal the internal pressures of two liquids are, the more miscible they are. The more unlike the internal pressures, the more immiscible are the liquids. By approximating the energy of vaporization with the heat of vaporization, and by using Trouton's rule, we may derive a quantity which is roughly proportional to the internal pressure, namely, the absolute boiling temperature divided by the molar volume of the liquid in cc.: $T_{b.p.}/V$. This quantity is tabulated for most of the solvents in Tables 12.1 and 12.2. When estimating solubilities by means of internal pressures, it is important to remember that the theory is applicable only to mixtures in which there are no chemical reactions or solvation effects. Thus, although ammonia and water have quite different internal pressures, they are infinitely miscible in one another. On the other hand, the solubility trends of saturated hydrocarbons (which are chemically inert to most of the solvents in Tables 12.1 and 12.2) are readily predictable from internal pressure considerations. For *n*-hexane, $T_{b.p.}/V = 2.6$, and, as one might expect, this liquid is practically insoluble in such liquids as water ($T_{b.p.}/V = 20.7$) and sulfuric acid ($T_{b.p.}/V = 11.3$). However, it does have a limited solubility in liquid ammonia ($T_{b.p.}/V = 9.6$) and hydrogen cyanide ($T_{b.p.}/V = 7.7$). Mercury has

[1] J. H. Hildebrand and R. L. Scott, "The Solubility of Nonelectrolytes," 3rd ed., Reinhold Pub. Corp., New York, 1950.

such a high internal pressure ($T_{b.p.}/V = 42.5$) that it is practically insoluble in all of the common solvents. White phosphorus, with $T_{b.p.}/V = 7.8$, is practically insoluble in water ($T_{b.p.}/V = 20.7$), slightly soluble in n-hexane ($T_{b.p.}/V = 2.6$), and very soluble in carbon disulfide ($T_{b.p.}/V = 5.3$).

SOLUBILITY OF ELECTROLYTES

If ions are considered as spheres of radius r and charge e and if the solvent is assumed to retain its macroscopic dielectric constant D in the vicinity of ions, then the energy of solution of an ion is given by the expression

$$\Delta E = -\left(\frac{e^2}{2r}\right)\left(1 - \frac{1}{D}\right).$$

Thus it is reasonable that electrolytes more readily dissociate into ions in solvents of high dielectric constant than in solvents of low dielectric constant. The solvents of high dielectric constant consist of polar molecules which orient themselves around ions. In polar solvents of low dielectric constant, salts often dissolve to give solutions in which there is practically no evidence for ionic dissociation. For example, a solution of lithium perchlorate in diethyl ether is only weakly conducting and the vapor-pressure lowering corresponds to a solution of undissociated molecules.[2] In these solutions, it is presumed that the ions are solvated with shells of solvent molecules, and that most of the electrolyte exists in the form of neutral ion-pairs.

Most of the protonic solvents (Table 12.1) are highly hydrogen bonded in the liquid state. This hydrogen bonding is reflected in abnormally high values for the entropy of vaporization *per mole of vapor*. For unassociated liquids, this quantity is usually about 21 entropy units. The entropies of vaporization in Table 12.1 are for one *formula weight* of solvent.

PURIFICATION AND HANDLING

The three non-aqueous inorganic solvents which are relatively safe to use and are commonly used are ammonia, sulfuric acid, and sulfur dioxide. Methods for purifying and using these solvents are discussed in the following paragraphs. The acid-base chemistry of these and other solvents has been discussed in Chapter 3. The chemistry of metal-ammonia solutions has been discussed in Chapter 4. For further discussions of the chemistry of non-aqueous solvents, the following books may be consulted:

L. F. Audrieth and J. Kleinberg, "Non-Aqueous Solvents," John Wiley and Sons, New York, 1953.

[2] K. Ekelin and L. G. Sillén, *Acta Chem. Scand.*, **7**, 987 (1953).

G. Jander, "Die Chemie in Wasserähnlichen Lösungsmitteln," Springer-Verlag, Berlin, 1949.

A. R. Pray, Chapter 3 in "Comprehensive Inorganic Chemistry," Volume 5, M. C. Sneed and R. C. Brasted, editors, Van Nostrand, Princeton, N. J., 1956.

A. Weissberger, E. Proskauer, J. Ridlick, and E. Toops, Jr., "Organic Solvents," 2nd ed., Interscience Publishers, New York, 1955.

LIQUID AMMONIA

Refrigeration-grade liquid ammonia contains less than 0.05 per cent water as the principal impurity. For many purposes, such ammonia is sufficiently pure. In such cases, the ammonia may be passed directly from the cylinder into the reaction vessel, which may be a Dewar, a refrigerated glass tube, and so on.[3] Ordinarily, the reaction vessel should be protected from the moisture and carbon dioxide of the atmosphere, but even this precaution may be neglected if these impurities are harmless. In fact, ammonia may be handled in ordinary glassware (beakers, flasks, Büchner funnels, and the like) if a good hood is available.

When even a trace of water would be detrimental, ammonia must be dried by dissolving sodium in it, followed by distillation. Such work is usually performed in a vacuum line, although a metal high-pressure system would function equally well.

Ammonia has a vapor pressure near ten atmospheres at room temperature. Sealed glass tubes of less than 20 mm. diameter will seldom burst under such a pressure; nevertheless, any glass tube containing liquid ammonia at room temperature should be handled with the greatest of care. (Face shield and thick gloves.) The reader is referred to Franklin[4] for a discussion of the types of reactions which may be performed by the use of sealed glass tubes containing liquid ammonia. By following the procedure described in Chapter 14 (under *Sealed-Tube Reactions*), sealed tubes containing ammonia may be safely heated to as high as 150°.

SULFURIC ACID

The most convenient way to make 100 per cent sulfuric acid is to add just enough fuming sulfuric acid (sulfuric acid containing excess SO_3) to ordinary 96 per cent sulfuric acid to convert all the water to sulfuric acid.

---

[3] See Appendix 6 for directions for drawing liquid ammonia from a cylinder.

[4] E. C. Franklin, "The Nitrogen System of Compounds," Reinhold Pub. Corp., New York, 1935, pp. 317–330.

The "fair-and-foggy" method[5] is used to determine the endpoint. In this remarkably simple yet delicate test, a gust of moist air is blown across the acid with a small rubber syringe. If the acid is more than 100 per cent pure (*i.e.*, contains excess SO_3), a fog will appear. If the acid is less than 100 per cent pure, no fog will appear. By this procedure, one may adjust the composition to within 0.02 per cent of pure sulfuric acid.

Sulfuric acid is extremely hygroscopic. If it is important that it remain anhydrous, it should be suitably protected from the atmosphere. It also should be remembered that hot sulfuric acid is a powerful oxidizing and dehydrating agent. Whenever more than a few milliliters of the hot acid must be handled, special protective shielding should be provided.

SULFUR DIOXIDE

Commercial sulfur dioxide contains trace amounts of sulfur trioxide and as much as 0.1 per cent water. Passage of the gas through concentrated sulfuric acid removes both of these impurities. The liquid may be handled in much the same way as used for ammonia. If small amounts of water are acceptable, ordinary Dewars and flasks may be used to contain the liquid. Otherwise, the vacuum line or closed tubes are recommended.

For the purpose of fulfilling the requirement "use of a non-aqueous solvent" as a special technique (see Chapter 6), certain trivial experiments will be excluded. For example, the use of alcohol as a solvent for recrystallizing a salt will not fulfill the requirement. Check with your instructor if you have any doubt about whether or not a particular experiment will satisfy the requirement.

SUGGESTED SYNTHESES INVOLVING NON-AQUEOUS SOLVENTS

H_2SO_4

sulfamic acid	H. F. Walton, "Inorganic Preparations," Prentice-Hall, Englewood Cliffs, N. J., 1948, pp. 135–137; W. G. Palmer, "Experimental Inorganic Chemistry," Cambridge University Press, 1954, p. 349.
nitryl chloride	M. Volpe and H. S. Johnston, *J. Am. Chem. Soc.*, **78**, 3903 (1956); R. Kaplan and H. Shechter, *Inorg. Syntheses*, **4**, 52 (1953).
potassium imidodisulfate $NH(SO_3K)_2$	Palmer, p. 352.

[5] J. E. Kunzler, *Anal. Chem.*, **25**, 93 (1953).

HOAc

> lead tetraacetate   Walton, pp. 138–140.

> red mercuric sulfide   { L. C. Newell, R. N. Maxson, and M. H. Filson, *Inorg. Syntheses*, **1**, 19 (1939).

SO₂

> sulfamic acid   { H. Sisler, M. Butler, and L. F. Audrieth, *Inorg. Syntheses*, **2**, 176 (1946).

NH₃

> hexamminechromium(III) nitrate and chloropentamminechromium(III) chloride

> { W. E. Henderson and W. C. Fernelius, "A Course in Inorganic Preparations," McGraw-Hill Book Co., Inc., New York, 1935, pp. 130–131.

> sodium amide   This text, p. 153.

> melamine   { P. McClellan, *Ind. Eng. Chem.*, **32**, 1181 (1940).

CHAPTER 13

IoN-EXCHANGE
COLUMNS

Ion-exchange Resins

Ion-exchange resins are porous, synthetic organic polymers containing charged groups which are capable of holding positive or negative ions. For example, Dowex-50 is a *cation exchanger* because it contains sulfonate groups whose negative charges must be neutralized by an equivalent number of cations. Amberlite IRA-400, Dowex-1 and Dowex-2 are *anion exchangers* because they contain quaternary ammonium groups whose positive charges must be neutralized by an equivalent number of anions. When a cation exchanger is in equilibrium with a solution containing the salts of two different metals, the relative amounts of the metal ions in the resin phase are determined by the relative concentrations of these ions in the bulk of the solution. The equilibrium may be expressed in terms of the mass-action law. For example, for Dowex-50, the equilibrium between Li^+ and Na^+,

$$Li^+_{(resin)} + Na^+ = Li^+ + Na^+_{(resin)} \qquad (13.1)$$

may be expressed by the relation

$$Q = \frac{(Li^+)(Na^+_r)}{(Li^+_r)(Na^+)} \approx 2 \text{ (at 25° and ionic strength 0.1)}. \qquad (13.2)$$

Equilibrium quotients of this type are useful for comparing the relative

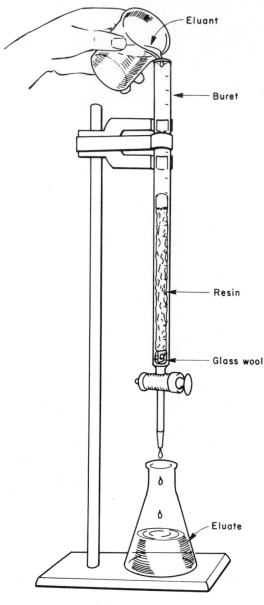

Eluant

Buret

Resin

Glass wool

Eluate

FIGURE 13.1.
A simple ion-exchange column.

affinities of a resin toward various ions. (Of course, similar quotients may be written for anion-exchange resins.)

Ion-exchange resins have two principal uses in synthetic chemistry: (1) the *replacement* of one ion by another, and (2) the *separation* of different kinds of ions from one another. In both cases, the resins are almost always used in a column. Let us consider the techniques involved in each case.

Replacement of One Ion by Another

Suppose that one is preparing a solution of tetraethylammonium hydroxide from a solution of tetraethylammonium chloride. One fills a column (such as pictured in Figure 13.1) with about twice as many equivalents of some anion exchanger such as Dowex-2 (equivalent weight *ca.* 300) as there are equivalents of chloride in the solution. Then a concentrated solution of sodium hydroxide is passed through the column to ensure the absence of any anions other than hydroxide in the resin, and the column is thoroughly rinsed with distilled water. Now the solution of tetraethylammonium chloride is allowed to percolate slowly through the column. The effluent, when combined with the small amount of solution still held in the column (which may be rinsed out with a little distilled water), should contain a quantitative yield of chloride-free tetraethylammonium hydroxide.

Separation of Ions

When a solution of the salts of several very similar metals is passed through a cation-exchange resin column (in which the resin is in, say, the hydrogen form), the metal ions will be held in the resin at the top of the column. If large volumes of a solution containing some other metal ion are now passed through the column, the original metal ions will gradually move down the column as they are displaced by the new metal ions. The ions which have the least affinity for the resin will move down the fastest and *vice versa*. As a consequence, the original ions will be separated into bands on the column and they may be separated by appropriate collection of the eluate.

A commoner method of separating cations on a column is to use an eluant which contains some substance which will complex the cations. The various cations will form complexes of various degrees of stability and will appear in the eluate in the order of decreasing complex stability. Rare earths, for example, may be fractionally eluted from a cation-exchange resin with a solution of tartrate or citrate.

An ion-exchange column which is being used to separate different ions may be thought of as a long series of successive solution-resin equilibria, or "theoretical plates." The reader is referred to Appendix 8 for a discussion of the theory of theoretical plates.

BIBLIOGRAPHY

General references

O. Samuelson, "Ion Exchangers in Analytical Chemistry," John Wiley and Sons, New York, 1953.

F. C. Nachod, ed., "Ion Exchange, Theory and Application," Academic Press, New York, 1949.

N. K. Hiester and R. C. Phillips, *Chem. Engineering*, **61**, 161 (1954).

Society of Chemical Industry, "Ion Exchange and its Applications," 1955.

Specific references

The Separation of Rare Earth, Fission Product and Other Metal Ions and Anions by Adsorption on Ion-Exchange Resins. *J. Am. Chem. Soc.*, **69**, 2769–2881 (1947).

The Separation of Cis- and Trans-Isomers of Complex Ions. King and Walters, *J. Am. Chem. Soc.*, **74**, 4471 (1952). Hougen, Schug, and King, *J. Am. Chem. Soc.*, **79**, 519 (1957).

Preparation of Polyphosphoric Acids and Their Tetramethylammonium Salts. Van Wazer, Griffith, and McCullough, *J. Am. Chem. Soc.*, **77**, 287 (1955).

Preparation of Monosilicic Acid. Alexander, *J. Am. Chem. Soc.*, **75**, 2887 (1953).

Preparation of Heteropolyacids. Baker, Loev, and McCutcheon, *J. Am. Chem. Soc.*, **72**, 2374 (1950).

Preparation of Complex Acids of Cobalt and Chromium. McCutcheon and Schuele, *J. Am. Chem. Soc.*, **75**, 1845 (1953).

PROBLEMS

For each pair of compounds listed below, give both a classical chemical method and an ion-exchange method for quantitatively converting one compound into the other (and *vice versa*).

1. KBr and KOH
2. NH_4NO_3 and HNO_3
3. $(NH_3OH)HSO_4$ and $(NH_3OH)Cl$.

CHAPTER 14

THE AUTOCLAVE

An autoclave (or high-pressure "bomb") is used for carrying out reactions with gases under high pressure and for handling solutions at temperatures above their boiling points. A typical laboratory autoclave is pictured in Figure 14.1. Auxiliary apparatus which may be used to charge the bomb with gas, to heat the bomb, and to rock the bomb is shown in Figure 14.2. The illustrated equipment[1] is similar to that used in most high-pressure laboratories, and so the following directions, although highly detailed, are of general applicability.

Instructions for Charging the Bomb with Gas

The bomb is always stored coated with oil in order to prevent rusting. So immediately before using the bomb, it is rinsed with several small portions of benzene, once with acetone, and is finally dried with a stream of air.

The clean bomb is set into the bomb vise. In placing the bomb in the vise, the position of the three holes in the bottom should be noted. The large center hole in the bottom of the bomb is for a holding screw, and the two small holes on either side are for a thermocouple and a heating jacket insert. The hole for the thermocouple is the smaller of the two.

The reactants are placed in the bomb. (Although the total capacity of the

[1] Manufactured by the American Instrument Co., Inc., Silver Spring, Md.

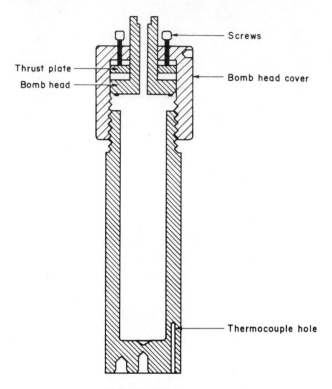

FIGURE 14.1.
High-pressure bomb.

bomb is 300 ml., the total volume of reactants, including solvent, should never exceed 140 ml.). The bomb head is placed on the top of the bomb and it is moved about gradually until the gasket slides into the recess provided for it. The thrust plate is then placed on the bomb head so that the side which has been previously exposed to the screws is on top. The bomb-head cover is screwed down gently until it almost touches the thrust plate and is then reversed one-half turn. (It is important that all the screws be slightly recessed into the bomb head cover before placing the cover on the bomb.) The head should not turn as the cover is screwed down. The screws are then turned down, using a small hex-wrench, until they just reach the thrust plate. The screws are tightened with a torsion wrench. (A torque of 20 foot-pounds should be used with a copper gasket, and a torque of 40 foot-pounds should be used with a stainless steel gasket.) In using a torsion wrench, one hand should be placed on the end attached to the screw so that a firm fit is had. The wrench should always be kept parallel to the table top in order not to

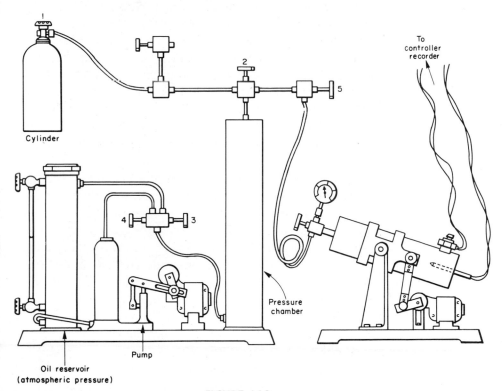

FIGURE 14.2.
Autoclave apparatus.

strip the screw or the fitting of the wrench. The screws should be tightened according to the following pattern:

<pre>
              3
        6   8
     1   5
        4   2
              7
</pre>

The tightening cycle is repeated until none of the screws move. *DO NOT USE MORE THAN THE RECOMMENDED TORQUE!* During this entire operation caution should be exercised that the bomb head does not move.

The gage is now attached to the bomb. This is done by holding the gage in one hand and screwing the pressure fitting with the other. A wrench should not be employed in this operation. The face of the gage should be parallel to an imaginary line through the three holes in the bottom of the bomb, with the gage overhanging the side of the bomb which is opposite the thermocouple hole. The gage and the bomb are now carefully lifted from the vise, holding the gage in one hand so it will not rotate freely. Do *not* support one end of the bomb by the gage. The bomb is placed into the heating jacket so that the side of the bomb with the thermocouple hole is on the bottom. In this way, the opposite hole will settle onto a fitting which protrudes from the bottom of the jacket. When properly fitted into the jacket, the top of the bomb head cover should be flush with the end of the heating jacket. The back-side of the gage is loosely attached by means of a thumb screw to the metal arm which extends from the jacket. Now, a small stiff metal rod, the size of the thermocouple, is inserted into the thermocouple hole in the bottom of the heating jacket in order to line up the bomb with the thermocouple hole. Next, the large screw is placed in the center hole in the rear of the heating jacket and it is tightened with a wrench, using gentle pressure, in order to hold the bomb in the heating jacket. Next, the gage is tightened to the bomb; this is most safely done by placing one wrench on the hex nut entering the bomb and one wrench (fixed wrench, *not* an adjustable one such as a crescent wrench) on the hex nut entering the gage. By gently applying pressure in opposite directions, one prevents excessive strain on the gage connection. It should be noticed that all fittings are of the high-pressure type and function by a good fit rather than by the application of excessive pressure. All that excessive pressure will do is spread the precision fitting and render it more susceptible to leaks. Finally, the thumb screw on the rear side of the gage is tightened.

The metal rod is removed from the thermocouple hole and the thermocouple carefully inserted. It should be placed so that it just touches the end of the well and then the end holder is firmly screwed in place.

Gas addition.[2] The coiled high-pressure tubing is put in place by screwing one end into needle valve 5 (see Figure 14.2) and the other end into the bottom of the gage valve. The needle valve on the gage and needle valve 5 are then closed. It should be remembered that a needle valve should only be turned gently and that excessive pressure should never be applied.

Use of the booster. Before any gas is added, it should be made sure that the oil in the glass side-arm is approximately at the upper etched line. If not,

---

[2] In the following discussion, it has been assumed that the gas cylinder pressure is lower than the desired starting pressure and that it will be necessary to use the booster pump. It has also been assumed that the compression cylinder has been previously flushed with the gas from the gas cylinder. When boosting is not required, the same directions apply, except that it is then never necessary to open valve 2 or to operate the pump.

valve 3 is carefully opened and the oil allowed to return slowly from the pressure chamber. It is imperative that this operation be done slowly since the presence of gas bubbles in the oil will stop the booster from working and the system will need to be primed. Valve 3 is then closed.

With all the other valves closed, valve 1 (the valve at the top of the gas cylinder) is opened. Next, valve 2 (on top of the compression cylinder) is slowly opened. This fills the compression cylinder to tank pressure. Valve 5 and the gage valve are then opened to allow the gas to fill the bomb. At this point, the bomb may be purged of air by closing valve 5 and loosening the connection between the coiled high-pressure tubing and valve 5. Retighten the connection and reopen valve 5.

Valve 1 is closed so that the booster and bomb system is isolated from the gas cylinder. *Next*, valve 4 is opened and *then* the pump is turned on. *If the motor is turned on before valve 4 is open*, it will *break the shaft* of the hydraulic pump, since it will be pumping against a closed system. The compressing of the gas is allowed to continue until the desired pressure is reached or until the oil level in the glass side-arm has reached the lower etched line. The motor should be shut off at this time, for excessive pumping at this point will fill the hydraulic system with air and the pump will not function. Valve 4 is closed.

If after one boosting the pressure still is not sufficiently high, the process must be repeated. This is done by closing valve 5. Valve 3 is carefully opened and the oil returned to the atmospheric reservoir and then the valve closed. Next, valve 1 is opened and the chamber filled with hydrogen from the tank and then valve 1 is closed. *Valve 4 is then opened* and the pump is turned on. After a short while valve 5 is *very slowly* opened and the pressure increase carefully watched. When the desired pressure is reached, first turn off the valve in the gage. Immediately turn off the motor of the booster, and then shut valves 4, 5, and 2. Next, return the oil to the atmospheric chamber through valve 3 and then close valve 3. Disconnect the coiled high-pressure tubing so that the shaker will be able to work.

Use of the temperature controller. After the above operations have been completed, the reactants are ready to be heated. The rocking motor and the recorder-controller are turned on. The pointer on the recorder-controller is set at the desired temperature, and the switch on the heating jacket is turned to HIGH. When a temperature about 30° below the desired temperature has been reached, it may be necessary to turn the switch to MEDIUM or LOW in order to obtain the smallest fluctuation in temperature. The apparatus should be watched until the temperature controller is working properly.

Opening bomb. The bomb is allowed to cool to room temperature (about two hours), the gas is vented (in a hood if poisonous), and the bomb is opened by reversing the procedure for closing. The bomb and head are lightly but thoroughly oiled after the product has been removed and the bomb has been cleaned.

General precautions. Do not smoke when working with inflammable gases such as H_2 or CO. Keep the autoclave room well ventilated and vent poisonous gases such as CO in a hood.

If anything gives way, it is likely to be the gage. Do not put your face near it; especially do not put your face *behind* the gage, for blow-out would most likely be to the rear.

Do not carry out a large-scale reaction which has not been tried on a small scale. (There may be a violent reaction in which the temperature and pressure increase uncontrollably.)

If anything is noticeably wrong with the equipment, report to your instructor at once. Especially, if the pressure screws in the head closure cannot be turned by hand, report to the instructor so that he can decide if they should be replaced.

Instructions for Sealed-tube Reactions

Occasionally it is desired to heat a solution above its boiling point when it would be undesirable for the reactants or products to come in contact with the metal parts of the bomb. In such cases, the solution is sealed in a glass ampoule, the ampoule is carefully packed into the bomb with the aid of glass wool, and about 50 ml. of the pure solvent is placed in the bomb. The bomb head is attached as previously described, but instead of attaching the gage, a closed plug is attached to the top of the bomb. The bomb may now be heated without having the glass ampoule burst. After cooling the bomb to room temperature, the ampoule may be removed and opened for recovery of the products.

BIBLIOGRAPHY

H. Adkins, "Reactions of Hydrogen," University of Wisconsin Press, 1937, Chapter 3.

Autoclave Syntheses

$[Co(CO)_4]_2$ I. Wender, H. Sternberg, S. Metlin, and M. Orchin, *Inorg. Syntheses*, **5**, 190 (1957).

$HCo(CO)_4$ *ibid.*, **5**, 194 (1957).

$HOSO_2NH_2$ H. Sisler, M. Butler, and L. F. Audrieth, *Inorg. Syntheses*, **2**, 176 (1946).

$Cr(CO)_6$ B. Owen, J. English, Jr., H. Cassidy, and C. Dundon, *Inorg. Syntheses*, **3**, 156 (1950).

$C_6H_{11}SiCl_3$ C. Burkhard and R. Krieble, *Inorg. Syntheses*, **4**, 43 (1953).

$W(CO)_6$ D. T. Hurd, *Inorg. Syntheses*, **5**, 135 (1957).

$Cr(CO)_6$ G. Natta, *et al.*, *J. Am. Chem. Soc.*, **79**, 3611 (1957).

$(NCNH_2)_3$ P. McClellan, *Ind. Eng. Chem.*, **32**, 1181 (1940).

CHAPTER 15

LIQUID-LIQUID
EXTRACTION

A simple solute dissolved in one phase in equilibrium with another, immiscible phase will distribute itself between the two phases so that the ratio of the activities in the two phases is a constant at a fixed temperature. If we are concerned with dilute solutions, we may make the approximation that the activity of a solute is proportional to its concentration, and we write

$$K = \frac{C_1}{C_2}.$$

The constant K is the *distribution constant*, and C_1 and C_2 are the concentrations in the two phases. The distribution constant is readily determined by shaking the solute with the two liquids in a separatory funnel, followed by analyses of the separated phases.

SINGLE-STAGE CONTINUOUS EXTRACTION

Unless the distribution constant is very large, a single extraction with a separatory funnel will not remove sufficient solute from the extrahend (the solvent from which the solute is extracted) if a reasonably quantitative separation is desired. Several successive extractions with fresh portions of extractant can be employed, but such a procedure is often tedious or involves excessive volumes of the extractant.

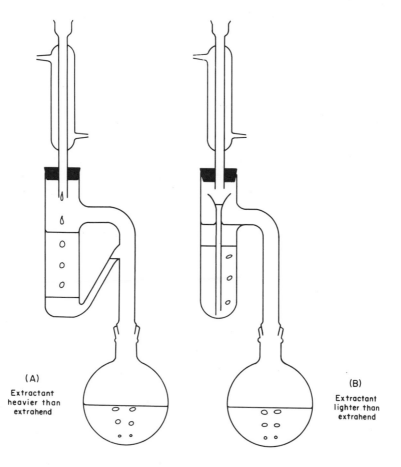

FIGURE 15.1.

Single-stage continuous extractors.

A *continuous extractor* often solves the problem. In this type of extractor the extractant is continuously furnished to the extrahend by distillation and passes through it.

There are two main types of continuous extractors: those in which the extractant must be lighter than the extrahend, and *vice versa*. These two types are pictured in Figure 15.1.

BATCHWISE COUNTERCURRENT EXTRACTION

Two solutes may be separated from each other by selective extraction if their distribution coefficients are sufficiently different. The efficiency of the extraction depends on the ratio of the distribution coefficients, or the *separation factor, S*:

$$S = K_x/K_Y.$$

If the separation factor is very large or very small (*e.g.*, 10^4 or 10^{-4}), the two solutes may practically be separated quantitatively by simple methods such as those discussed above. But if the separation factor is near unity, special schemes must be devised for fractionally extracting the solutes. One of the most effective procedures is that known as countercurrent extraction. The procedure described below is more accurately described as "batchwise counter-current extraction with center feed." The reader is referred to the article by L. C. and D. Craig in Weissberger (2nd ed., Vol. III, Part I) for an extensive description of other fractional extraction schemes. A discussion of the concept of theoretical plates as applied to separation schemes is given in Appendix 8.

Imagine a series of nine equilibration stages as pictured in Figure 15.2.

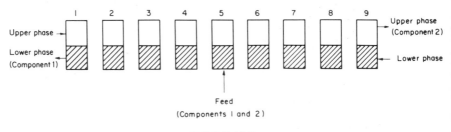

FIGURE 15.2.

Countercurrent extraction with center feed (nine stages).

First a mixture of the two solutes is distributed between the two phases in stage 5. Then the upper phase is placed in stage 6 with fresh lower phase and the lower phase is placed in stage 4 with fresh upper phase. Again, a mixture of the two solutes is placed in stage 5 with fresh phases. Now the three stages are equilibrated. The upper phase moves from stage 6 to stage 7, from stage 5 to stage 6, and from stage 4 to stage 5. The lower phase moves from stage 4 to stage 3, from stage 5 to stage 4, and from stage 6 to stage 5. Fresh upper phase is put in stages 3 and 4, and fresh lower phase is put in stages 6 and 7. Now all five stages are equilibrated and the cycle is repeated over and over. After four cycles, lower phase is ejected from stage 1 and upper phase is ejected from stage 9. If the relative volumes of the two countercurrent phases have been properly chosen, the effluent lower phases will contain much more of one solute than the other and the effluent upper phase will contain much more of the other than the one.

Many cycles must be performed before the concentrations of solutes in the effluents reach their steady-state values. The closer the separation factor is to unity the more stages are required in order to effect a "quantitative" separation of the two solutes. Usually the volumes of the two phases are adjusted so that the following relation holds: $V_1/V_2 = 1/\sqrt{K_x K_y}$.

Figure 15.3 gives another way of schematically representing a counter-current extraction. In this figure five stages are involved, requiring only three separatory funnels. Suppose we are separating two substances, X and Y, which are preferentially extracted by ether and water, respectively. In separatory funnel 1 we

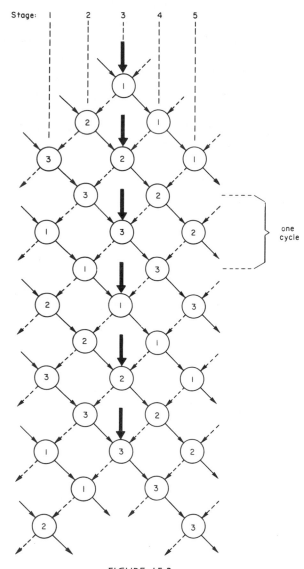

FIGURE 15.3.

Concurrent extraction with center feed (five stages).

mix and equilibrate the mixture of X and Y (feed) with portions of ether and water. The aqueous phase is drained into funnel 2; ether is added to funnel 2, and then funnel 2 is shaken. While funnel 2 is settling, water is added to funnel 1 and funnel 1 is shaken. The aqueous phase in funnel 2 is drained into funnel 3; ether is added to funnel 3, and funnel 3 is shaken. The aqueous phase in funnel 1 is drained into funnel 2; another feed sample is introduced into funnel 2, and funnel 2 is shaken. Water is added to funnel 1 and funnel 1 is shaken. The aqueous phase is drained from funnel 3 into a beaker. This is the first product emerging from the fractionation, and it should be relatively rich in component Y. The aqueous phase is drained from funnel 2 into funnel 3 and funnel 3 is shaken. The aqueous phase from funnel 1 is drained into funnel 2 and funnel 2 is shaken. The ether phase remaining in funnel 1 may now be transferred to a beaker; this sample is the first X-enriched product. Fresh ether is now put in funnel 1 and funnel 1 reenters the scheme at stage 1.

BIBLIOGRAPHY

L. C. Craig and D. Craig, "Technique of Organic Chemistry," A. Weissberger, Ed., Interscience Publishers, New York, Vol. III, Part I, 1956, p. 149.

G. H. Morrison and H. Freiser, "Solvent Extraction in Analytical Chemistry," John Wiley and Sons, New York, 1957.

L. Alders, Ed., "Liquid-liquid Extraction. Theory and Laboratory Practice," 2nd ed., Van Nostrand, New York, 1959.

CHAPTER 16

SYNTHESES

In this chapter, directions are given for the preparation of eighteen different compounds. Each of the special techniques discussed in Chapters 7–15 is represented at least once in these syntheses. (See Table 16.1.) However, not all of the syntheses were chosen to illustrate special techniques—some are included simply because the compounds synthesized are particularly interesting. Although these syntheses could conceivably form the basis for a laboratory course in synthetic chemistry, it is recommended that they be used sparingly. Students not only enjoy seeking out synthetic methods in the literature, but it is also good for them to do so.

TABLE 16.1

Syntheses

Synthesis	Special Techniques Involved
1. $CuCl$	——
2. $K_2S_2O_8$	Electrolysis
3. $H_4SiW_{12}O_{40} \cdot 7H_2O$	Liquid-liquid extraction
4. $Na_5P_3O_{10}$; $H_5P_3O_{10}$	High temperature; ion exchange
5. AgO	Electrolysis; vacuum manipulation
6. $[(CH_3)_2SiO]_x$	——
7. O_3	Silent electrical discharge
8. $NaNH_2$	Non-aqueous solvent; inert atmosphere box
9. $TiCl_4$	High temperature
10. Al_2I_6	High temperature

TABLE 16.1 (continued)

11. B_2H_6 Vacuum manipulation
12. $Sn(C_6H_5)_4$ Non-aqueous solvent
13. Sm_2O_3; Nd_2O_3;
    Pr_6O_{11}; La_2O_3 Ion exchange
14. S_4N_4 Non-aqueous solvent; Soxhlet extraction
15. $Co_2(CO)_8$ Autoclave
16. Ge_2Cl_6 Microwave discharge
17. $(PNCl_2)_x$ Non-aqueous solvent
18. $Fe(C_5H_5)_2$ Non-aqueous solvent

Each of the syntheses has been checked by the author and his students. They are listed in what is believed to be the order of increasing difficulty. It is suggested that, before a student starts to work on a synthesis, he be required to answer the questions posed at the end of the synthesis. Most of the estimates of "total time required" are in terms of three-hour laboratory periods. The lists of "special apparatus required" refer to apparatus which is not in the student's locker (see Appendix 9).

1. *The Preparation of Copper(I) Chloride*[1]

$$2\ Cu^{2+} + 2\ Cl^- + SO_3^{2-} + H_2O \longrightarrow 2\ CuCl + SO_4^{2-} + 2\ H^+.$$

Total time required: $1\frac{1}{2}$ hours

Actual working time: $1\frac{1}{2}$ hours

Preliminary study assignment:

W. M. Latimer and J. H. Hildebrand, "Reference Book of Inorganic Chemistry," 3rd ed., Macmillan, New York, 1951, pp. 107–109.

Reagents required:

13 g. $CuCl_2 \cdot 2\ H_2O$

12 g. Na_2SO_3

3 ml. conc. HCl

100 ml. glacial acetic acid

100 ml. absolute alcohol

100 ml. ether

PROCEDURE:

Slowly add a solution of 10 g. of sodium sulfite in 50 ml. of water to a well-stirred solution of 13 g. of copper(II) chloride 2-hydrate in 20 ml. of water. Add the resulting suspension to a liter of water in which 1 g. of sodium sulfite and

[1] Essentially the same directions are given by Keller and Wycoff in *Inorganic Syntheses*, **2**, 1 (1946). Used by permission of the McGraw-Hill Book Co., New York.

2 ml. of concentrated hydrochloric acid have been dissolved; stir the mixture well and allow it to stand until all the copper(I) chloride has settled. Carefully decant the supernatant solution and quickly wash the precipitate onto a sintered-glass suction filter with about 500 ml. of water containing 0.5 g. of sodium sulfite and 1 ml. of concentrated hydrochloric acid. Take care that a layer of liquid covers the salt in the funnel at all times.

Wash the product five times with 20-ml. portions of glacial acetic acid. During this washing process adjust the suction so that the wash liquid is sucked through slowly. When only a thin film of liquid covers the solid, add the next portion of glacial acetic acid. Wash the walls of the funnel each time with the washing liquid. Follow the glacial acetic acid washing with three 30-ml. washings with absolute alcohol and six 15-ml. washings with ether in exactly the same way. After the last portion of ether has been removed fairly completely by applying suction for about 30 seconds, transfer the white solid to a dry watch glass and place in an oven (75–100°) for about 25 minutes. The product may be preserved in a tightly stoppered test tube. A yield of about 6.5 g. (85 per cent) is usually obtained.

Pure copper(I) chloride is white, but moist air converts it into a dark-green material of composition $CuCl_2 \cdot 3\ Cu(OH)_2$.

QUESTIONS:

1. By what other methods may copper(I) chloride be prepared?

2. What species are formed when copper(I) chloride is dissolved (*a*) in aqueous ammonia? (*b*) in concentrated hydrochloric acid?

3. Why is the product finally washed with alcohol and then with ether?

2. *The Preparation of Potassium Peroxydisulfate*

$$2\ HSO_4^- \longrightarrow S_2O_8^{2-} + 2\ H^+ + 2\ e^-.$$

Total time required: 2 laboratory periods

Actual working time: 3 hours

Preliminary study assignment:

Chapter 7. *Electrolytic Syntheses*
W. M. Latimer and J. H. Hildebrand, "Reference Book of Inorganic Chemistry," 3rd ed., Macmillan, New York, 1951, pp. 261, 264.

Reagents required:

> 40 g. $KHSO_4$
> 2-*l*. beaker full of crushed ice
> 25 ml. 95 per cent alcohol
> 10 ml. ether
> 150 ml. standardized 0.1 N $S_2O_3^{2-}$
> 8 g. KI
> 2 ml. glacial acetic acid

Special apparatus required:

> D.C. power supply
> Insulated wire for connections
> Platinum-wire electrode (1 cm. long; 0.64 mm. diam.)
> Platinum-foil electrode
> Large-diameter test tube (35 mm. diam.; 6 in. tall)
> Crystallizing dish ($7\frac{1}{2}$ in. diam.)

PROCEDURE:

Saturate 80 ml. of water at about 5° with potassium hydrogen sulfate, $KHSO_4$, making sure that no excess solid is present. (About 35 g. of $KHSO_4$ will suffice.) Place this solution in the large test tube, and assemble the platinum-wire anode and platinum-foil cathode as shown in Figure 16.1. Surround the test tube with an ice bath, and pass a current of about 1.5 amp for two hours. Collect the precipitate on a small sintered glass funnel without using any wash water. Dry the crystals with suction; wash, successively, with alcohol and ether, and dry in the desiccator for a day or two. Weigh the dry product.

The material may be analyzed by the following procedure. Dissolve a 0.25 g. sample in 30 ml. of water, add 4 g. of potassium iodide, stopper the flask, and swirl to dissolve the iodide. After allowing the solution to stand for at least fifteen minutes, add 1 ml. of glacial acetic acid and titrate the liberated iodine with standard thiosulfate. At least two samples should be analyzed.

Calculate the current efficiency, taking account of the fact that the product is not 100 per cent pure.

QUESTIONS:

1. By following the above procedure, a student prepared 3.0 grams of potassium peroxydisulfate. A 0.2703 gram sample of the material required 18.85 ml. of 0.1020 N thiosulfate. What was the current efficiency?

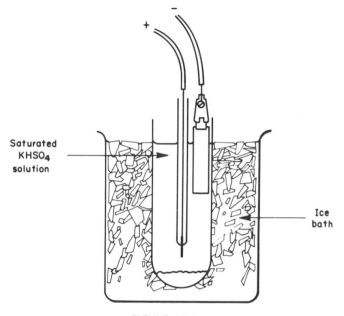

FIGURE 16.1.
Apparatus for electrolytic preparation of $K_2S_2O_8$.

2. Why must the solution of peroxydisulfate and iodide be allowed to stand for fifteen minutes before adding acid and titrating?

3. How might one prepare peroxymonosulfuric acid? What are the structures of the peroxymonosulfate and peroxydisulfate ions?

3. *The Preparation of 12-Tungstosilicic Acid*[2]

$$12 \, WO_4^{2-} + SiO_3^{2-} + 26 \, H^+ \longrightarrow H_4SiW_{12}O_{40} \cdot xH_2O + (11-x)H_2O.$$

Total time required: 2 laboratory periods

Actual working time: 5 hours

Preliminary study assignment:

H. J. Eméleus and J. S. Anderson, "Modern Aspects of Inorganic Chemistry," 3rd ed., Van Nostrand, New York, 1960, Chapter IX.

[2] This procedure is adapted from one given by E. North, *Inorg. Syntheses,* **1,** 129 (1939).

Reagents required:

50 g. $Na_2WO_4 \cdot 2 H_2O$
2.7 ml. sodium silicate solution (water glass of density 1.38 or 40° Bé.)
65 ml. conc. HCl
50 ml. diethyl ether
About 150 ml. standardized 0.1 N NaOH
Methyl orange indicator

Special apparatus required:

Small motor-driven stirrer

PROCEDURE:

Dissolve the sodium tungstate(VI) 2-hydrate in 100 ml. of water and then add the sodium silicate solution. Vigorously stir the solution and hold at incipient boiling while adding 30 ml. of concentrated hydrochloric acid drop-wise from a dropping funnel. This operation should take about ten minutes. After filtering and cooling the solution, add 20 ml. more of concentrated hydrochloric acid. Then shake the solution in a separatory funnel with 35 ml. of ether. (If three liquid phases do not form, it will be necessary to use a little more ether.) Withdraw the bottom layer of oily ether complex into a beaker, and discard the other two phases. Rinse out the separatory funnel and return the ether complex to the funnel along with a solution of 12 ml. of concentrated hydrochloric acid in 38 ml. of water and about 10 ml. of ether. After shaking the mixture, run the lower phase into an evaporating dish and allow it to stand in a drafty hood for a day or two. Dry the remaining crystals in an oven at 70° for two hours. Avoid touching the moist crystals with a metal spatula; otherwise they may turn blue. A yield of 32 g. is generally obtained.

Weigh out two 2-gram samples of the material and titrate their aqueous solutions with 0.1 N NaOH, using methyl orange as an indicator. The equivalent weight should agree closely with the value 751, corresponding to the tetrabasic acid $H_4SiW_{12}O_{40} \cdot 7 H_2O$.

QUESTIONS:

1. How many structurally different kinds of oxygen atoms are there in the basic 12-tungstosilicate ion (exclusive of water of hydration)? How many oxygen atoms are there of each kind?

4. The Preparation of Sodium Triphosphate and Triphosphoric Acid

$$NaH_2PO_4 \cdot H_2O + 2\ Na_2HPO_4 \cdot 12\ H_2O \longrightarrow Na_5P_3O_{10} + 15\ H_2O$$
$$5\ Na^+ + P_3O_{10}{}^{5-} + 5\ H^+{}_{(resin)} \longrightarrow H_5P_3O_{10} + 5\ Na^+{}_{(resin)}.$$

Total time required: 2 laboratory periods

Actual working time: 3 hours

Preliminary study assignment:

Chapter 5. *Structure from Chemical Data*
Chapter 8. *High Temperature Processes*
Chapter 13. *Ion-exchange Columns*
J. R. Van Wazer, "Phosphorus and its Compounds," Vol. I, Interscience Publishers, New York, 1958.

Reagents required:

1.5 g. $NaH_2PO_4 \cdot H_2O$
7.8 g. $Na_2HPO_4 \cdot 12\ H_2O$
1 M HCl
150 ml. standardized 0.1 N NaOH
About 50 ml. of Dowex-50 Ion Exchange Resin, 20–50 mesh
Standard buffer solution (pH 4 or 7)

Special apparatus required:

Platinum crucible, 10 ml.
Muffle furnace
pH meter

PROCEDURE:

Place an intimate mixture of the two phosphates in a platinum crucible. (If hydrates different from those indicated are used, adjust the amounts so that the mole ratio of dihydrogen phosphate to monohydrogen phosphate is kept at 1:2.) Heat the mixture at 540° to 580° for two hours and then allow it to cool in the air.

Wash the cation-exchange resin into a 50 ml. buret which has a glass-wool plug at the bottom. (See Figure 13.1.) Take care that the liquid level never falls below the top of the resin bed. Convert the resin to the hydrogen form by allowing about 500 ml. of 1 M HCl to percolate through it. Remove the hydrochloric acid by washing the resin with distilled water until the eluate gives no test for chloride with silver ion. Weigh out about 0.25 g. of the sodium triphosphate and dissolve it in 20 ml. of water. Allow this solution, followed by 200 ml. of water, to percolate slowly through the column into a 500-ml. beaker. Standardize the pH meter, dip the rinsed electrodes into the triphosphoric acid solution, and titrate the solution with standardized 0.1 N NaOH. Record the pH of the solution after each 1-ml. addition of base (more frequently at the endpoints). Plot the pH against the volume of base added and, from the endpoints, estimate the average chain length for the acid.

QUESTIONS:

1. Give two methods for separating a mixture of sodium polyphosphates of different chain length.

2. How would you distinguish cyclotriphosphate from a very high molecular weight straight-chain polyphosphate?

5. *The Preparation of Silver(II) Oxide*[3]

$$Ag^+ + H_2O \longrightarrow AgO + 2 H^+ + e^-.$$

Total time required: 3 laboratory periods

Actual working time: 4 hours

Preliminary study assignment:

Chapter 7. *Electrolytic Syntheses*
Chapter 10. *The Vacuum Line*
W. Latimer and J. Hildebrand, "Reference Book of Inorganic Chemistry," 3rd ed., Macmillan, New York, 1951, pp. 116–117, 121–122.

Reagents required:

35 g. AgNO$_3$
50 ml. conc. HNO$_3$
Ice

Special apparatus required:

D.C. power supply
Insulated wire for connections
Platinum-foil electrodes (2 × 10 cm. and 1 × 8 cm.)
Stirring motor and stirrer
Tube with sintered-glass disk
Crystallizing dish (7½ in. diam.)
Vacuum manifold

[3] See A. Noyes, D. DeVault, C. Coryell and T. Deahl, *J. Am. Chem. Soc.*, **59**, 1326 (1937).

PROCEDURE:

Approximately 150 ml. of 1.5 *M* HNO_3 containing 35 g. of $AgNO_3$ is placed in a 250 ml. beaker surrounded by an ice bath. A cathode cup containing about 30 ml. of 10 *M* HNO_3 is partially immersed, and the platinum-foil electrodes and stirrer are assembled as shown in Figure 16.2. A current of

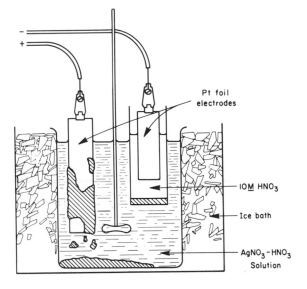

FIGURE 16.2.
Apparatus for the electrolytic preparation of AgO.

3 amps is passed for two hours, after which the precipitate of $Ag_7O_8NO_3$ is filtered off on a fritted glass funnel and washed with water. This material is then converted to AgO by boiling in water for two hours; the AgO is filtered off and dried in a desiccator at room temperature.

The AgO may be analyzed by measuring the oxygen evolved when a sample is heated *in vacuo*. Weigh out 0.1 g. of the material into a glass tube with a ball joint; attach to the vacuum line, and evacuate. Connect the Toepler pump and heat the AgO with a torch until no more oxygen is pumped by the Toepler pump. (It is best to have a liquid nitrogen trap between the sample and the Toepler pump.) From the amount of oxygen collected and the weight of the sample, the purity may be calculated.

QUESTIONS:

1. What is the reaction which takes place when silver(II) oxide is heated *in vacuo*?

2. A student obtained 55.0 ml. of oxygen (at 158 mm. pressure and 25°) from the decomposition of a 0.1239 g. sample of silver(II) oxide. What was the empirical formula of the sample, on the assumption that the only impurity was silver(I) oxide?

6. The Preparation of Cyclic Polymers of Dimethylsiloxane[4]

$$x(CH_3)_2SiCl_2 + x\ H_2O \longrightarrow [(CH_3)_2SiO]_x + 2\ xH^+ + 2\ xCl^-.$$

Total time required: 2 laboratory periods

Actual working time: 5 hours

Preliminary study assignment:

E. G. Rochow, "An Introduction to the Chemistry of the Silicones," 2nd ed., John Wiley and Sons, New York, 1951, pp. 78–88.

J. Cason and H. Rapoport, "Laboratory Text in Organic Chemistry," Prentice-Hall, Englewood Cliffs, N. J., 1950, pp. 232–259 (discussion of fractional distillation).

Reagents required:

50 ml. $(CH_3)_2SiCl_2$ [5]
50 ml. diethyl ether
Ice

Special equipment required:

Small electric stirrer
Small fractional-distillation apparatus
Infrared lamp

PROCEDURE:

Place a solution of the dimethyldichlorosilane and ether in a dropping funnel whose tip reaches almost to the bottom of a 250 ml. beaker containing 100 ml. of water. Slowly add the solution through the funnel while vigorously stirring the water. Throughout the addition, hold the reaction mixture at 15° to 20° by surrounding the beaker with an ice bath. Separate the two phases with a

---

[4] See W. Patnode and D. F. Wilcock, *J. Am. Chem. Soc.*, **68**, 358 (1946).

[5] Dimethyldichlorosilane is commercially available, or it may be prepared from silicon and methyl chloride (*Inorg. Syntheses*, 3, 56 (1950).)

separatory funnel; discard the lower phase, and transfer the upper phase to the pot of the fractional-distillation apparatus. The first fraction to come over is ether (b.p. 34.6°). *CAUTION: keep flames away while distilling the ether!* The second fraction is the trimer of dimethylsiloxane, hexamethylcyclotrisiloxane (b.p. 134°). Since this fraction is a solid at room temperature (m.p. 64°), it will probably be necessary to stop the flow of water in the condenser and to warm the delivery tube with an infrared lamp in order to prevent clogging of the apparatus. The third fraction is the tetramer, octamethylcyclotetrasiloxane (b.p. 175°). Usually this is the last pure fraction which can be obtained from a distillation at atmospheric pressure. Attempts to collect further fractions usually result in such a high pot temperature that the high molecular weight diols of the type

$$HO[Si(CH_3)_2O]_xSi(CH_3)_2OH$$

are pyrolyzed to cyclic dimethylsiloxanes and water. Thus a cloudy distillate (a mixture of the trimer, tetramer, and water) is obtained.

Excluding any material formed by pyrolysis, the usual yields of trimer and tetramer are 3 and 16 grams, respectively. These yields may be augmented by a second fractionation of the crude pyrolysis product.

QUESTIONS:

1. If undiluted dimethyldichlorosilane is added to water, smaller yields of the low polymers of dimethylsiloxane are obtained than if the above directions are followed. Offer an explanation.

2. In what way does the preparation of "silicone oils" differ from the above synthesis? Explain the reason for the difference.

7. *The Preparation of Ozone*

$$^3/_2 O_2 \longrightarrow O_3.$$

Total time required: 1–2 laboratory periods

Actual working time: 3–5 hours

Preliminary study assignment:

Chapter 11. *Electrical Discharge Tubes.*

W. Latimer and J. Hildebrand, "Reference Book of Inorganic Chemistry," 3rd ed., Macmillan, New York, 1951, pp. 33–34.

Reagents required:

Depends upon what is to be done with the ozone.

Special apparatus required:

   High-voltage (A.C.) power supply
   Ozonizer

NOTICE:

The high-voltage power supply is not to be connected to the power line except by the instructor. The power supply must be used under the direct supervision of the instructor. Great care must be taken in order to avoid electrocution.

EXPERIMENTAL:

Ozone may be prepared by passing oxygen through the ozonizer while a potential of about 15 kv. is applied. There are various experiments that might be performed.

   1. It is instructive to determine the yield and concentration of the ozone as a function of either the flow-rate of oxygen or the applied potential. Ozone may be analyzed by allowing it to react with a potassium iodide-ammonium chloride solution:

$$2\ NH_4{}^+ + O_3 + 3\ I^- \longrightarrow I_3{}^- + O_2 + H_2O + 2\ NH_3.$$

The ozone may be completely removed from an oxygen stream by allowing it to pass through a gas-washing bottle containing a solution which is 0.1 molar in NH_4Cl and 0.1 molar in KI. The resulting triiodide solution may be titrated with standard thiosulfate solution.

   2. Ozone has been used to oxidize elements to their highest oxidation states in aqueous solution without chemical contamination. For example, the Pu^{3+} ion may be oxidized by ozone in acid solution to the plutonyl ion, $PuO_2{}^{2+}$. (This oxidation cannot be carried out by hydrogen peroxide, since the latter reagent is oxidized by the plutonyl ion.) The oxidizing power of ozone has been used to advantage in the quantitative analyses of manganese and iodine. Manganese can be quantitatively oxidized to permanganate by ozone if the oxidation is carried out in 1.5 M $HClO_4$, using Ag^+ as catalyst (*ca.* 50 mg. $AgNO_3$/100 ml.). Iodide is quantitatively oxidized to periodate in concentrated NaOH or KOH solutions.

   3. Various volatile oxides may be prepared by treatment of lower oxides with ozone. For example, the following conversions may be effected:

$$NO_2 \xrightarrow{\ O_3\ } N_2O_5$$
$$NOCl \xrightarrow{\ O_3\ } NO_2Cl$$
$$SO_2 \xrightarrow{\ O_3\ } S_2O_7.$$

8. *The Preparation of Sodium Amide*

$$Na + NH_3 \longrightarrow NaNH_2 + {}^1/_2 H_2.$$

Total time required: 2 laboratory periods

Actual working time: 4 hours

Preliminary study assignment:

Chapter 4. *Some Special Types of Reaction (The Chemistry of Metal Ammonia Solutions)*
Chapter 9. *Handling Materials in an Inert Atmosphere*
Chapter 12. *Non-aqueous Solvents*
Appendix 6. *Compressed-gas Cylinders*

Reagents required:

150 ml. liquid ammonia
10 g. chunk of sodium
Crystal of $Fe(NO_3)_3 \cdot 9\ H_2O$
150 ml. of standardized 0.1 N HCl
150 ml. of standardized 0.1 N NaOH
Methyl red indicator

Special apparatus required:

Wide-mouthed, unsilvered Dewar flask (300–400 ml.), equipped with special stopper and addition tube as shown in Figure 16.3.
Inert atmosphere box (argon- or nitrogen-filled)

PROCEDURE:

In the inert atmosphere box, scrape the chunk of sodium clean of oxide and oil with a knife. Then cut about 5 grams into pea-sized pieces and put them into the addition tube. After attaching a short piece of large-diameter tubing to the tube and clamping it closed with a pinch clamp, it may be brought out into the air.

Pass the outlet tube of an ammonia cylinder through the larger opening in the top of the Dewar and flush ammonia gas through the Dewar for a minute or so by barely opening the cylinder valves. Then open the valves further and collect about 150 ml. of liquid ammonia in the Dewar. Close the valves, remove the Dewar from the ammonia cylinder, and add a small crystal (about the size of a small rice kernel) of $Fe(NO_3)_3 \cdot 9\ H_2O$ to the ammonia. Attach the addition tube by means of the rubber tubing, and

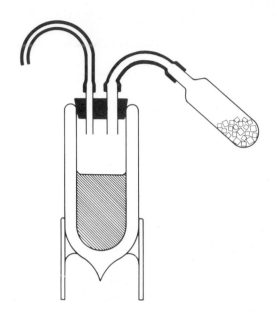

FIGURE 16.3.
Apparatus for the preparation of NaNH$_2$.

attach a two-foot length of rubber tubing to the smaller opening at the top of the Dewar. Now add the pieces of sodium at a rate such as to maintain a moderate effervescence of the ammonia solution. About half an hour after adding all the sodium, the blue color of the solution should disappear. The addition tube with its rubber tube may then be removed and a rubber stopper placed in the tube at the top of the Dewar. Let the apparatus stand for a day or two while the ammonia evaporates. Then place the entire apparatus in the lock of the inert atmosphere box and thoroughly evacuate the lock. Move the apparatus into the box; and, with the aid of a long spatula, transfer the sodium amide from the Dewar to a tightly capped bottle. At the same time it may be convenient to transfer a small analytical sample of the product (about 0.05–0.08 g.) to a previously weighed weighing bottle. The weighing bottle may then be removed from the box and reweighed to determine the weight of sample taken. (If the bottle was originally weighed while containing air, a correction must be made for the different weight of the inert gas.) Quickly add the entire analytical sample to excess standard acid and back-titrate the solution with standard base, using methyl red as the indicator.

QUESTIONS:

1. What is the purpose of the iron(III) nitrate?

2. How many ml. of 0.1 N HCl are equivalent to 0.08 g. of sodium amide?

3. Why cannot phenolphthalein be used as the indicator in the titration?

9. *The Preparation of Titanium Tetrachloride*[6]

$$TiO_2 + 2C + 4Cl_2 \longrightarrow TiCl_4 + 2COCl_2.$$

Total time required: 3 laboratory periods

Actual working time: 6 hours

Preliminary study assignment:

Chapter 8. *High Temperature Processes*
H. Rémy (J. S. Anderson, trans.), "Treatise on Inorganic Chemistry," Vol. II, Elsevier, New York, 1956, pp. 57–58.

Reagents required:

24 g. TiO_2 powder
8 g. carbon black
Chlorine cylinder
Nitrogen cylinder
ca. 10 g. cottonseed or linseed oil
Fibrous asbestos or glass wool
A few copper turnings

Special apparatus required:

Glass reaction tube
Tube furnace and Variac
Thermocouple
Potentiometer
3″ × 3″ iron sheet
100-ml. distilling flask

PROCEDURE:

Intimately mix the titanium dioxide and the carbon black in an iron crucible, and add just enough cottonseed or linseed oil to make a stiff paste. After

[6] See H. F. Walton, "Inorganic Preparations," Prentice-Hall, Englewood Cliffs, N. J., 1948, pp. 107–109.

thoroughly mixing these materials, cover the crucible with the flat piece of sheet iron and slowly heat, in the hood, with the Fisher burner. Gradually increase the temperature until no more fumes are evolved and the crucible is red hot. Allow the crucible to cool while covered and then break up the porous mass into small pieces. Pack these pieces into the Pyrex tube, using plugs of fibrous asbestos or glass wool to hold the material in place. Attach a one-hole stopper with a glass tube to the large end of the reaction tube and pass nitrogen through the tube, while heating to about 500°. When all the moisture has been driven from the mixture of TiO_2 and carbon, stop the heating and allow the tube to cool while still passing the nitrogen. If two hours of working time are not then available, tightly stopper both ends of the tube to protect the reactants from moisture.

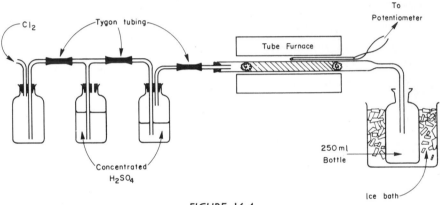

FIGURE 16.4.
Apparatus for preparation of $TiCl_4$.

Set up the apparatus in a hood as shown in Figure 16.4. Pass chlorine at a rate such that about three to four bubbles per second form in the sulfuric acid trap. Hold the temperature of the furnace at 550° (no higher, or the glass may melt). When it appears that no more titanium tetrachloride is condensing in the receiving bottle, stop the flow of chlorine and turn off the furnace. Add a few copper turnings to the liquid, stopper the bottle, and let stand for a day or two. Then decant the $TiCl_4$ into the distilling flask, distill the liquid (b.p. 136.4°), and collect and store the distillate in a glass-stoppered bottle. A yield of about 30 g. of product is usually obtained.

QUESTIONS:

1. Why is the crude titanium tetrachloride stored over copper metal for a day or two?

2. Name three other volatile chlorides which may be made by a method analogous to that used here for titanium tetrachloride.

10. *The Preparation of Aluminum(III) Iodide*

$$2 \text{ Al} + 3 \text{ I}_2 \longrightarrow \text{Al}_2\text{I}_6.$$

Total time required: 3 laboratory periods

Actual working time: 8 hours

Preliminary study assignment:

Chapter 8. *High Temperature Processes*
T. Moeller, "Inorganic Chemistry," John Wiley and Sons, New York, 1952, pp. 749–751.

Reagents required:

5 g. aluminum turnings
10 g. iodine

Special apparatus required:

$2\frac{1}{2}$ ft. of 22 mm. tubing
Tube furnace and Variac
Thermocouple
Potentiometer
Vacuum pump

PROCEDURE:

Fashion the glass tube into the shape shown in Figure 16.5. Place the aluminum and iodine near the middle of the main tube and seal off the large end of the tube. Attach the 8 mm. tube to a vacuum pump (protected with an intervening cold trap or tube containing NaOH pellets) and evacuate the apparatus to 0.5 mm. or lower. Seal off the apparatus at a point some 4 inches from the collection bulb and place it in the tube furnace as shown, with the aluminum in the center of the furnace. Raise the furnace temperature to 500° and repeatedly sublime the iodine from one end of the tube to the other by means of a Bunsen burner. When the iodine has completely reacted, remove the tube from the furnace and sublime all the Al_2I_6 into the collection tube. (Take care that the constriction does not become plugged.) Seal off the collection tube and discard the main reaction tube.

A portion of the Al_2I_6 may be sublimed into the narrow tube projecting from the collection tube and a two-inch length of this narrow tubing may be

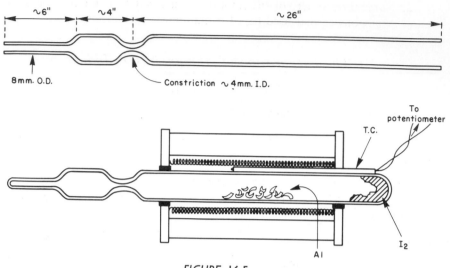

FIGURE 16.5.

Apparatus for the preparation of Al_2I_6.

sealed off. This small sample of material may now be used for a melting-point determination and, if desired, for analysis. The reported melting point of aluminum iodide is 191°; the boiling point is 386°.

QUESTIONS:

1. What is the structure of the Al_2I_6 molecule?

2. The cryoscopic molecular weights of aluminum(III) halides in benzene correspond to the dimers (Al_2X_6). However, the molecular weights in ether correspond to the monomers (AlX_3). Explain.

11. *The Preparation of Diborane*[7]

$$KBH_4 + H_2SO_4 \longrightarrow {}^1/_2 B_2H_6 + H_2 + K^+ + HSO_4^-.$$

Total time required: $1\frac{1}{2}$ laboratory periods
Actual working time: 4 hours

Preliminary study assignment:

Chapter 4. *Some Special Types of Reaction* (*Hydride Syntheses*)
Chapter 10. *The Vacuum Line*
Appendix 2. *Cold Baths*

[7] H. G. Weiss and I. Shapiro, *J. Am. Chem. Soc.*, **81**, 6167 (1959).

Reagents required:

> 0.5 g. KBH_4
> 20 ml. conc. H_2SO_4
> 2 drops of Dow Polyglycol P1200 (optional)
> Liquid nitrogen

Special apparatus required:

> 200-ml., two-neck flask with "tipping tube" and adapter.
> Vacuum manifold
> Magnetic stirrer and stirring bar

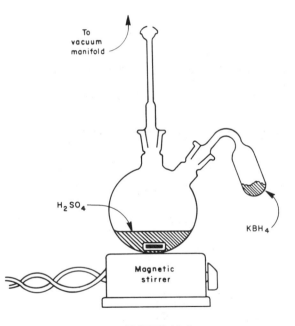

To
vacuum
manifold

H_2SO_4

KBH_4

Magnetic
stirrer

FIGURE 16.6.
Apparatus for the preparation of B_2H_6.

PROCEDURE:

Connect the two-neck, 200-ml. flask (with the adapter) to the vacuum line below cock 5. (Figure 10.1.) Place twenty ml. of 96 per cent H_2SO_4 containing two drops of Dow Polyglycol P1200 and a glass- or teflon-covered stirring bar in the flask and connect the "tipping tube" containing 0.5 g. of potassium hydroborate. Mount the magnetic stirrer below the flask. (See Figure 16.6

for a picture of the set-up.) While stirring the sulfuric acid, evacuate the flask to a pressure of 10 microns or less. Then immerse trap *B* in liquid nitrogen and gradually add the potassium hydroborate to the stirred sulfuric acid. Pump off the evolved hydrogen through cock 12; the condensable gases (B_2H_6 plus a little SO_2) will condense in trap *B*. It is not necessary to pump on the system continually during the hydroborate addition; in fact, the reaction goes more smoothly if the pressure is maintained at about 10 cm. When all the hydroborate has been added, however, thoroughly evacuate the system and close cock 5. Purify the diborane by allowing it to pass from trap *B* through trap *C* (cooled to $-112°$) to trap *D*. Determine the volume of diborane formed, and measure its vapor pressure at the temperature of melting carbon disulfide. (Literature v.p. = 225 mm.)

QUESTIONS:

1. What is the most likely impurity in diborane which has been prepared and purified by the above procedure? How might it be removed?

2. How may one safely and conveniently dispose of diborane?

12. *The Preparation of Tin Tetraphenyl*

$$2\,Na + C_6H_5Cl \longrightarrow C_6H_5Na + NaCl$$

$$4\,C_6H_5Na + SnCl_4 \longrightarrow (C_6H_5)_4Sn + 4\,NaCl.$$

Total time required: 3 laboratory periods

Actual working time: 7 hours

Preliminary study assignment:

Chapter 12. *Non-Aqueous Solvents*
Appendix 6. *Compressed-gas Cylinders*
G. E. Coates, "Organo-Metallic Compounds," Methuen & Co., London, 1956, pp. 118–133.
T. P. Whaley, *Inorg. Syntheses*, **5**, 6 (1957).

Reagents required:

275 ml. dry toluene (350 ml. if wet)
35 ml. chlorobenzene
15 g. sodium
10 ml. $SnCl_4$

Special apparatus required:

> 500-ml., three-neck, round-bottom flask
> Two Variacs
> Heating mantle
> High-speed stirring motor
> Stirring rod with sharp metal blades
> Cylinder of argon
> About 1000 ml. of kerosene in pan
> Extra sintered-glass funnel and filter flask
> "Dry ice"

PROCEDURE:

Fifteen grams of clean sodium chunks and 250 ml. of dry toluene[8] are placed in the flask. A thermometer and an argon inlet tube are inserted through one of the side arms of the flask. The other side arm is stoppered. The stirrer is inserted through the main mouth of the flask—take care that the stirring blades cannot hit the thermometer and that the stirring blades are above the chunks of sodium. While stirring gently, and with a slow stream of argon flowing, heat the contents slowly to 105°. Then lower the stirrer so that the blades are about 1 cm. from the bottom of the flask and turn the stirrer on full power. It will be found necessary to increase the power input to the heating mantle in order to keep the temperature at 105°. After about 10 minutes of vigorous stirring at 105°, remove the heating mantle from the flask. When the temperature has fallen to 99°, stop the stirrer and allow the flask to cool to room temperature. The sodium should now be in the form of a fine sand. Stir the solution gently to see if any of the particles have agglomerated. If so, the process must be repeated. If the sodium dispersion is not to be used immediately, thoroughly flush the flask with argon and tightly stopper it.

Using the heating mantle, heat the dispersion, with moderately vigorous stirring, to 45°. Attach a dropping funnel containing 35 ml. of chlorobenzene to the unused side arm and add 2–3 ml. of the chlorobenzene to the flask. *NOTICE:* The flask should never contain more than 3 ml. of unreacted chlorobenzene! If more than this amount is present, an uncontrollably vigorous reaction may take place, resulting in a fire.

Remove the heating mantle from the flask. The reaction should start, as evidenced by a rise in the temperature. If the reaction does not start at 45°, cautiously raise the temperature to 50° (no higher!). If the reaction starts at this

---

[8] Toluene may be dried by simple distillation. Put about 350 ml. in the distilling flask and discard the initial cloudy distillate and the last 25 ml.

temperature, the temperature may suddenly rise to as high as 55°, so be ready to cool the flask quickly with the kerosene bath.[9] (If the reaction does not , start at 50°, cool the flask to room temperature, cautiously hydrolyze the mixture with alcohol, and discard.)

Temperatures in excess of 50° will cause no great harm at the beginning of the synthesis, but thereafter the temperature must be kept below 45°; keep the flask partially immersed in the kerosene bath and cool the kerosene bath by occasionally adding pieces of "dry ice" to it. The temperature of the reaction mixture may be held between 40–45° by adjusting the rate of addition of chlorobenzene.

After all the chlorobenzene has been added (about 1–2 hours), place a solution of 10 ml. of stannic chloride in 25 ml. of toluene in the dropping funnel and, over a period of 30 minutes, add this solution to the reaction flask. During this addition, it is necessary to cool the flask so as to keep the temperature below 45°. The flask may now be stored indefinitely (without protection from the air) until the tin tetraphenyl is extracted from the mixture.

Wipe the kerosene from the bottom of the flask, and with moderate stirring, heat the mixture to incipient boiling and quickly filter through a sintered-glass funnel. It is best to keep most of the solid residue in the reaction flask. Cool the filtrate to room temperature and filter off the product on another sintered-glass funnel. Return the filtrate to the original flask and repeat the extraction twice. The final solution should be cooled in an ice-bath before filtering. Suck the crystals of tin tetraphenyl as dry as possible on the filter and then let air-dry for 4–20 hours on a watch glass.

A yield of about 25 grams of material melting at 226–8° should be obtained. A purer product (melting at 229°) may be obtained by recrystallization from benzene or toluene.

QUESTIONS:

1. By what other methods may tin tetraphenyl be prepared, and in what ways is the present method superior?
2. What by-products will be formed if the reaction mixture is allowed to get too warm?

13. *The Separation of Samarium, Neodymium, Praseodymium, and Lanthanum by Ion Exchange*
(Two students)

Total time required: 5 laboratory periods
Actual working time: 12 hours

[9] Never use a water bath. In fact, keep water entirely away from the experimental set-up.

PROCEDURE:

Add 700 ml. of dry carbon tetrachloride[11] and 25 ml. of disulfur dichloride ("sulfur monochloride") to a one-liter, round-bottom, three-neck flask. Insert a paddle stirrer through the main neck and a gas inlet tube through one of the side necks, as shown in Figure 16.9. While stirring briskly, pass

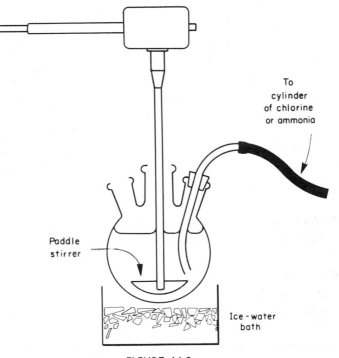

FIGURE 16.9.
Apparatus for the preparation of S_4N_4.

chlorine into the solution until a distinctly green layer of chlorine gas is observed over the solution. Then stop the flow of chlorine and connect the gas delivery tube to a cylinder of ammonia. Immerse the flask in an ice-bath, and pass ammonia through the stirred solution. Pass the ammonia as rapidly as possible, without causing material to splash from the flask.

Initially, copious white fumes will form. However, these will soon disappear and a thick yellow-brown suspension will form in the flask. The color then changes to grey-green, brown, grey, and finally, after about $2\frac{1}{2}$ hours, salmon-red. At this point, stop the ammonia flow. During the

[11] Carbon tetrachloride may be dried by allowing it to stand over anhydrous calcium sulfate (Drierite) for several days.

passage of ammonia, much of the carbon tetrachloride will evaporate. Maintain a constant volume of liquid in the flask by occasionally adding carbon tetrachloride through the third neck of the flask.

Filter the reaction mixture on a sintered-glass funnel, and slurry the solid material with 500 ml. of water for about 10 minutes. Filter off the remaining solid and allow it to air-dry thoroughly for a day or two.[12]

To remove S_7NH, shake the dried residue with 150 ml. of ether for ten minutes. Decant off and discard the solution, and repeat the process. Place the dry residue in an extraction thimble and extract with 250 ml. of dry dioxane[13] in a Soxhlet extractor until the eluate is only weakly colored orange-yellow (4–5 hours). Then allow the apparatus to cool slowly to room temperature. Some of the S_4N_4 will crystallize out in the extraction pot. Filter off these crystals, and evaporate the filtrate to dryness for a second crop of crystals. The first batch of crystals is generally quite pure. However, if it is desired that they be further purified, they may be combined with the second batch of less pure crystals and recrystallized from benzene. A yield of 16 grams is generally obtained. The pure material melts with decomposition at 179°.

CAUTION: Sulfur nitride should be handled with care, inasmuch as it will often explode when struck or when heated above 100°.

QUESTIONS:

1. What would be the effect of passing ammonia into the reaction mixture for several hours longer than required to give the red-salmon color?

2. In what way are S_8, S_7NH, S_4N_4, and $S_4N_4H_4$ structurally similar?

15. *The Preparation of Dicobalt Octacarbonyl*[14]

$$2 \, CoCO_3 + 2 \, H_2 + 8 \, CO \longrightarrow [Co(CO)_4]_2 + 2 \, H_2O + 2 \, CO_2.$$

Total time required: 2 laboratory periods

Actual working time: 5 hours

[12] The filtrate from the filtration of the original reaction mixture may be evaporated to dryness at room temperature to give a small amount of a mixture of yellow sulfur crystals and orange sulfur nitride crystals. This mixture may be added to the solid material described above.

[13] Allow 300 ml. of commercial dioxane to reflux over about 30 grams of sodium-lead alloy for several hours, and then distill 250 ml. of the dried dioxane.

[14] Essentially the same directions are given by Wender, Sternberg, Metlin, and Orchin in *Inorganic Syntheses*, **5**, 190 (1957). Used by permission of the McGraw-Hill Book Co., New York.

Preliminary study assignment:

Chapter 14. *High Pressure Apparatus*
T. Moeller, "Inorganic Chemistry," John Wiley and Sons, New York, 1952, pp. 700–717.

Reagents required:

7.5 g. $CoCO_3$
75 ml. low-boiling petroleum ether
Cylinder of carbon monoxide with at least 400 P.S.I. pressure.
Cylinder of hydrogen with at least 1700 P.S.I. pressure.
Cylinder of nitrogen

Special equipment required:

300-ml. stainless-steel autoclave and accessory equipment (described in Chapter 14).
Refrigerator with freezing compartment

PROCEDURE:

Place the petroleum ether and cobalt(II) carbonate in the autoclave. Following the general procedure outlined in Chapter 14, flush the autoclave three times with carbon monoxide and then fill it with carbon monoxide to a pressure of 1700 P.S.I. Turn the booster pump off and close all the valves. Replace the carbon monoxide cylinder with the hydrogen cylinder. With the valve attached to the gage closed, flush the system with hydrogen. Fill the pressure chamber with hydrogen at cylinder pressure, and close the cylinder valve (valve 1). Open the gage valve and boost the pressure to 3500 P.S.I. The autoclave now contains approximately equimolar amounts of hydrogen and carbon monoxide. Turn off the booster pump and close all the valves. Start the rocking mechanism and heat the autoclave to 150–160°. After holding the temperature in this range for 3 hours, stop the agitation and heating. When the autoclave has reached room temperature (after about 4 hours), carefully vent and open it in a hood. Pour the dark solution into a large beaker and filter it through filter paper into a 125-ml. Erlenmeyer flask. Store the flask overnight in the freezing compartment of a refrigerator, whereupon large, well-formed crystals of the product will form. Decant the solvent, and dry the crystals by passing a stream of dry nitrogen through the flask for several minutes. A yield of approximately 6 g. of dark-red crystals is usually obtained. The material melts at 50–51°, decomposing to black $[Co(CO)_3]_4$. If a sample is stored in an evacuated tube, it will slowly sublime, forming bright-orange crystals on the walls.

QUESTIONS:

1. Describe two other synthetic methods which have been used for preparing metal carbonyls.

2. How may cobalt carbonyl hydride be prepared?

16. *The Preparation of Digermanium Hexachloride*

$$2 GeCl_4 \longrightarrow Ge_2Cl_6 + Cl_2.$$

Total time required: 2 laboratory periods

Actual working time: 4 hours

Preliminary study assignment:

Chapter 11. *Electrical Discharge Tubes*

Reagents required:

2 ml. $GeCl_4$
ca. 300 ml. conc. HCl

Special apparatus required:

Microwave discharge apparatus (Figure 11.2)

PROCEDURE:

Assemble the apparatus as pictured in Figure 11.2. (Use Kel-F grease on the ground joints and stopcocks.) Place the germanium tetrachloride in a glass ampoule and connect the ampoule below one of the needle valves. Evacuate the main part of the apparatus, and, by momentarily opening the needle valve, pump the air from the ampoule. Immerse the first trap in an ice-HCl slush (*ca.* −18°), the second trap in a dry ice-acetone slush (−78°), and the third trap in liquid nitrogen.

By turning the needle valve, adjust the pressure in the system to about 0.5 mm. of Hg (6.5 mm. of dibutyl phthalate). Turn on the air jet (to cool the resonance cavity); turn on the fans (to cool the magnetron); and turn on the power to the magnetron. If a discharge does not form spontaneously, momentarily turn on the Tesla coil. When the discharge is established, increase the pressure (by further opening the needle valve) to as high a value as possible without causing the discharge to go out. When practically all of the germanium tetrachloride has vaporized (after about one hour), close the needle valve and turn off the power to the magnetron.

The glass tubing immediately beyond the discharge will contain polymeric germanium chlorides. The $-18°$ trap will contain crystals of Ge_2Cl_6; the $-78°$ trap will contain unreacted $GeCl_4$, and the liquid-nitrogen trap will contain chlorine. With a torch, seal off the entrance side (left side) of the $-18°$ trap and then seal off the exit side (right side). The trap containing the Ge_2Cl_6 will now be free. Keep it partially immersed in the cold bath until the ends of the trap cool to room temperature. Close all the cocks of the apparatus; remove all the cold baths, and, finally, remove the traps.

The Ge_2Cl_6 may be sublimed from one end of the sealed trap to another by simply cooling one end in an ice bath. Sublime half of the material into one end and half into the other end. Cool one end in an HCl-ice bath and the other end in liquid nitrogen, and let the tube stand for several minutes. Melt the bend in the tubing with a torch and separate the two ends. (Keep each end in its cold bath until the seals have cooled.) The end which was cooled in the HCl-ice bath should contain pure Ge_2Cl_6, uncontaminated with $GeCl_4$. Determine the melting point of this sample. Pure Ge_2Cl_6 melts at $41–42°$.

QUESTIONS:

1. What are the physical properties of C_2Cl_6 and Si_2Cl_6? How are these compounds prepared?

2. Suggest a new method for preparing digermane.

17. The Preparation of Trimeric and Tetrameric Phosphonitrilic Chloride

$$PCl_5 + NH_4Cl \longrightarrow PNCl_2 + 4 HCl.$$

Total time required: 4 laboratory periods

Actual working time: 9 hours

Preliminary study assignment:

Chapter 12. *Non-aqueous Solvents*
N. L. Paddock and H. T. Searle, *Advances in Inorganic Chemistry and Radiochemistry*, **1**, 347 (1959).

Reagents required:

300 ml. tetrachloroethane
120 g. PCl_5
38 g. NH_4Cl
300 ml. benzene

Special apparatus required:

 Electrically heated oil bath; Variac

 Extra 500-cc. distilling flask

 Special vacuum-distillation apparatus (Fig. 16.10).

 Portable vacuum pump

CAUTION: The phosphonitrilic chlorides and their derivatives are toxic materials and should be handled only in a hood.

PROCEDURE:

Add the ammonium chloride, phosphorus pentachloride, and tetrachloro-ethane to a 1000-ml. flask equipped with a reflux condenser. Attach a calcium chloride-filled drying tube to the top of the condenser. Immerse the flask in the oil bath and adjust the bath temperature to 135°. Keep the temperature at this value for 8–15 hours. After bringing the reaction products to room temperature, filter off the unreacted ammonium chloride and transfer the solution to a 500-cc. distilling flask. Set up for a vacuum distillation (using a second distilling flask as a receiver) and remove the solvent at as low a temperature as possible under a pressure of 10 mm. or less. A water bath should be used for the heating; its temperature should be kept below 50°. Transfer the remaining butter-like mass to a fritted glass funnel, where most

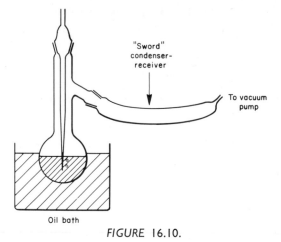

FIGURE 16.10.

Apparatus for fractional distillation of phosphonitrilic chlorides.

of the adhering oil is removed by suction. Use about 20 ml. of ice-cold benzene to help carry over the last bits of solid and to extract the remaining oil. Recrystallize the remaining solid from benzene. Transfer the recrystal-lized product to the special distilling flask (Figure 16.10) and, using an air-cooled "sword" condenser-receiver, fractionally distill at a pressure of approximately 10 mm. The trimer should distill at a bath temperature around 135° and the tetramer at a bath temperature around 190°. It may be necessary to warm the upper part of the distilling column in order to avoid plugging with solid product. (After collecting the trimer, lift the distilling flask from the bath so that it may cool slightly, and replace the condenser-receiver with a clean one. Then continue the distillation to collect the tetramer.)

The melting points of the trimer and tetramer are 114° and 123.5°, respectively.

QUESTIONS:

1. How may the so-called "inorganic rubber" be obtained?

2. How may the phosphonitrilic fluorides be prepared?

18. *The Preparation of Ferrocene*[15]

[Bis(cyclopentadienyl)iron(II)]

$$C_2H_5Br + Mg \longrightarrow C_2H_5MgBr$$

$$C_2H_5MgBr + C_5H_6 \longrightarrow C_5H_5MgBr + C_2H_6$$

$$2\,C_5H_5MgBr + [Fe(C_5H_7O_2)_2(C_5H_5N)_2] \longrightarrow [Fe(C_5H_5)_2] +$$
$$Mg(C_5H_7O_2)_2 + MgBr_2 + 2\,C_5H_5N.$$

Total time required: 4 laboratory periods, one of which must last 4–5 hours

Actual working time: 11 hours

Preliminary study assignment:

Chapter 12. *Non-aqueous Solvents*
Appendix 6. *Compressed-gas Cylinders*
G. Wilkinson and Γ. A. Cotton, *Progress in Inorganic Chemistry*, **1**, 1 (1959).
J. Cason and H. Rapoport, "Laboratory Text in Organic Chemistry," Prentice-Hall, Englewood Cliffs, N. J., 1950 (Section on Grignard reactions).

[15] This procedure is adapted from one given by G. Wilkinson, P. L. Pauson, and F. A. Cotton, *J. Am. Chem. Soc.*, **76**, 1970 (1954).

Reagents required:

19 g. $FeSO_4 \cdot 7 H_2O$ (or 16.5 g. $FeSO_4 \cdot 5 H_2O$)
60 ml. pyridine
25 ml. acetylacetone (2,4-pentanedione)
400 ml. ether
32 ml. ethyl bromide
10 g. clean, bright magnesium turnings
550 ml. benzene
50 ml. dicyclopentadiene
Cylinder of nitrogen or argon
About 20 g. "Drierite"
About 20 g. Na-Pb alloy or about 2 g. Na wire
250 ml. methanol
Ice
25 ml. conc. HCl

Special apparatus required:

2-liter, 3-neck (standard taper joints), round-bottom flask
Standard taper condenser
Paddle stirrer with air-tight seal
Standard taper dropping funnel with pressure equalization, 250 cc.
All-glass fractional distillation apparatus
100-ml. pipet

PROCEDURE:

To a saturated aqueous solution of 19 g. of iron(II) sulfate 7-hydrate (about 25–30 ml. of water is required) add 20 ml. of pyridine and 25 ml. of acetylacetone. Stir the mixture vigorously for several minutes and then filter off the dark-brown crystals on a sintered-glass filter and wash with 10 ml. of cold water. Dissolve the crystals in a minimum amount of hot pyridine (35 ml. will probably suffice); add 40 ml. of water, and cool in an ice bath. Filter off the crystals; dry them as thoroughly as possible by applying suction to the filter, and air-dry for a day or two. A yield of 17 g. is usually obtained. This coordination compound, bis(acetylacetonato)bis(pyridine)iron(II), has the formula

$$Fe(C_5H_7O_2)_2(C_5H_5N)_2.\ [16]$$

Assemble the round-bottom flask with the condenser, the dropping funnel, and the stirrer with the air-tight seal as in Figure 16.11. A glass tube (connected with flexible tubing to the nitrogen cylinder) is passed down through the condenser and the apparatus is flushed with nitrogen. While flushing with

[16] B. Emmert and R. Jarczynski, *Chem. Ber.*, **64**, 1072 (1931).

nitrogen, momentarily remove the dropping funnel and add 300 ml. of dry ether[17] and the clean, bright magnesium turnings to the flask.

CAUTION: Keep flames away from the apparatus!

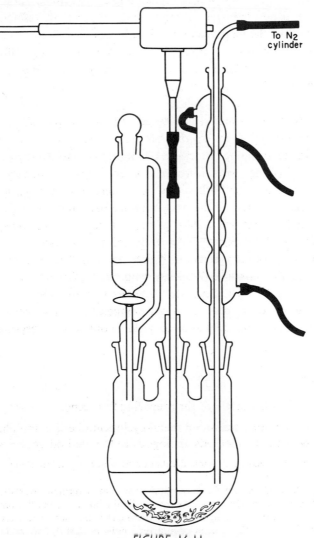

FIGURE 16.11.

Apparatus for the preparation of ferrocene.

[17] Let 400 ml. of ether stand for several days in a flask with a poorly-fitting glass stopper over about 2 g. of sodium wire or 20 g. of sodium-lead alloy. Without disturbing the layer of sodium hydroxide which settles out, pipet (using the house vacuum line) the ether from this flask and transfer it to the reaction vessel. Never pour anhydrous ether.

Place the ethyl bromide in the dropping funnel. Stop the flow of nitrogen, start the stirrer, and add about 5 ml. of ethyl bromide through the dropping funnel. Within a few minutes, the reaction should begin, as evidenced by the refluxing of the ether. Then add the remaining ethyl bromide at a rate such as to maintain gentle refluxing. If necessary, continue the refluxing on the steam bath until all the magnesium has dissolved.

NOTE: The following procedure should be followed without interruption until after the cyclopentadiene is added. If it is necessary to keep the Grignard reagent overnight, flush the apparatus with nitrogen and seal it from the atmosphere.

While flushing the system with nitrogen, momentarily remove the dropping funnel and add 300 ml. of dry benzene.[18] Place 37 ml. of dry cyclopentadiene[19] in the dropping funnel and add it dropwise to the stirred solution, while slowly flushing with nitrogen. After complete addition of the cyclopentadiene, warm the flask with a 50° water bath until the solution no longer effervesces. Then cool the flask in an ice bath and, through the dropping funnel, add a solution of 16 g. of the bis(acetylacetonato)bis(pyridine) iron(II) in 200 ml. of dry benzene. Allow the solution to stand for at least one hour at room temperature; then pour it onto about 400 g. of crushed ice and thoroughly stir the mixture. While stirring, add 300 ml. of 2 M HCl, and allow the ice to melt. Separate the phases. Filter the organic phase and evaporate it to dryness at room temperature. The crude product may be crystallized from methanol to yield about 4 g. of crystals melting at 173–174°.

QUESTIONS:

1. Give four other methods for preparing ferrocene.

2. Name four other transition metal-cyclopentadiene compounds which may be made by methods analogous to the method described here.

[18] Benzene may be dried by a simple distillation in which the initial cloudy distillate is discarded.

[19] Allow 50 ml. of 90 per cent dicyclopentadiene to stand overnight over about 20 g. of anhydrous calcium sulfate (Drierite). Decant the liquid into a round-bottom flask and slowly distill through a fractionating column, collecting only that which refluxes below 44°. (Cyclopentadiene boils at 42.5°; dicyclopentadiene boils at 170°.) This cyclopentadiene must be used within two or three hours, or an appreciable amount of dimerization will occur.

APPENDICES

---

1. *Glass Blowing*

It is practically essential for a synthetic inorganic chemist to be able to blow glass. Even if a professional glass blower is available, a chemist will save much time by making simple apparatus himself.

Practically all laboratory glassware is made of borosilicate glass (*Pyrex* or *Kimax*). This glass is remarkably resistant to thermal shock and does not soften until about 560°. A gas-oxygen flame is required when working this glass. You will have access to a gas-oxygen hand torch. This torch may be clamped to the bench top so that the hands are free to manipulate glassware in the flame, or the torch may be held in the hand so that glassware which is rigidly mounted may be blown.

Closed round ends. The procedure for forming a closed rounded end on a piece of glass tubing is illustrated in Figure 17.1. First a piece of cane is fused to the end of the tube for a handle, as in (B). Then the tubing is rotated evenly in a small, hot flame so that a short section near the end is heated. A thickened, constricted section will form (as shown in (C)) While the glass is still hot, the two ends are pulled apart, as shown in (D). The tapered end is then rotated in the flame to complete the seal and the narrow connecting tubing is pulled off. If this operation is properly performed, careful heating and blowing will yield a hemispherical end, as shown in (F). If too much glass is left on the end, the end wall will be too thick, as shown in (G). Excess

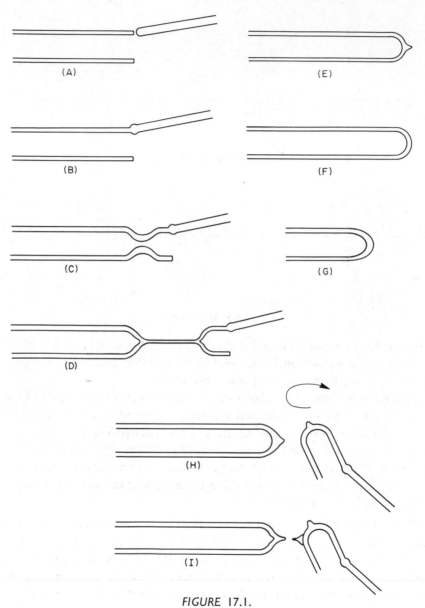

FIGURE 17.1.
Forming a closed rounded end on a piece of tubing.

glass may be removed by briefly touching a cold piece of glass to the hot end, as shown in (H) and (I).

End-to-end seals. The simplest end-to-end seal is that between tubes of equal bore. The outer end of one tube is closed with a cork, or otherwise sealed. The ends to be sealed are heated in the flame until they are soft, and are then gently pressed together, as in Figure 17.2 (A). It is important that good contact be made around the entire joint. The joint is then heated with

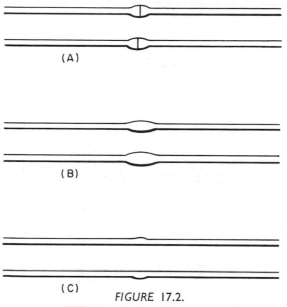

FIGURE 17.2.
Making a simple end-to-end seal.

occasional blowing to make a leak-proof seal, as in (B). While the glass is still hot, the seal is blown and elongated slightly. If properly done, the result is a single straight tube of uniform diameter and bore, as shown in (C).

The procedure for joining two tubes of unequal bore is the same as that described above, except that the diameter at the end of the larger tube must first be made equal to that of the smaller tube. This is accomplished by first making a closed round end, as in Figure 17.3 (A). The center of the closed end is then heated with a small, hot flame, and a small bulge is blown, as in (B) of Figure 17.3. The end of this bulge is similarly heated, and a large, thin bubble is blown out and broken off, as in (C) and (D) of Figure 17.3.

T-*connections.* A small area on one side of the tube which is to form the cross-piece is heated with a small, hot flame, and a bulge is blown, as shown in (A) of Figure 17.4. The very end of the bulge is similarly heated and blown out to a thin bubble which is broken off, as in (B) and (C) of Figure 17.4. The resulting hole and the end of the other piece of tubing are heated and joined, as in (D). By alternately heating and blowing various points of the seal, a strong, smooth union is obtained, as in (E).

General instructions. When blowing glass, it should be remembered that the hottest portions of the glass respond to pressure or movement most readily. Thus, if glass is blown while in the flame, the thin parts become still thinner. Soon after glass is removed from the flame, the thin portions, which

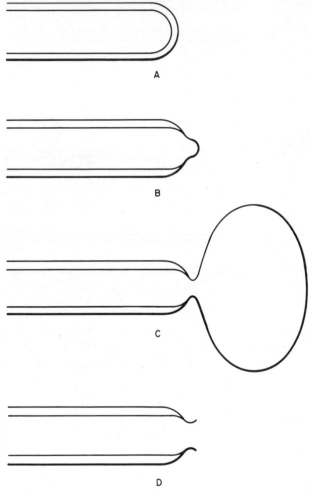

FIGURE 17.3.

Reducing the diameter at the end of a glass tube.

cool more rapidly, become inflexible, and blowing works out the thick parts. It is convenient to blow glassware through a piece of rubber tubing, one end of which is connected to the only open end of the glassware.

After blowing a piece of glassware, it should be cooled down to room temperature slowly, particularly so through the annealing region (500–600°).

This may be crudely accomplished by heating the glassware in a bushy flame while gradually reducing the oxygen supply.

The two commonest troubles encountered by the beginning glassblower are: (1) he does not heat the glass to a high enough temperature, and (2)

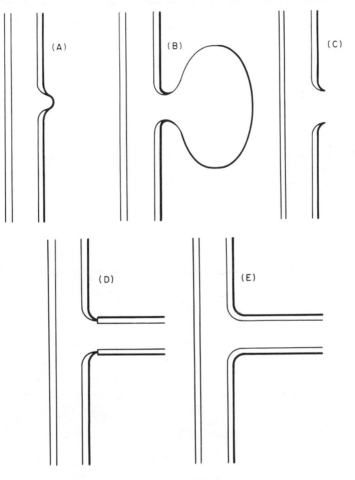

FIGURE 17.4.
Making a T-connection.

he has difficulty, when making seals, in holding the two pieces as if they were one. The first trouble usually results from the uncomfortably bright light which glass imparts to the flame when it is at the temperature required for blowing. This difficulty may be eliminated by simply wearing goggles made of didymium glass. The second trouble may be eliminated by clamping the pieces to be joined on a ring stand. In other words, the torch, and not the pieces of glass, is moved. (However, one of the glass pieces should be loosely clamped so that it may be slightly moved during the start of the seal.)

The following references may be helpful:

R. T. Sanderson, "Vacuum Manipulation of Volatile Compounds," John Wiley and Sons, New York, 1948, Chapter 3, pp. 14–29.

R. E. Dodd and P. L. Robinson, "Experimental Inorganic Chemistry," Elsevier, New York, 1954, pp. 90–97.

R. H. Wright, "Manual of Laboratory Glass-blowing," Chemical Publ. Co., Brooklyn, N. Y., 1943.

J. Strong, "Procedures in Experimental Physics," Prentice-Hall, Englewood Cliffs, N. J., 1944.

J. D. Heldman, "Techniques of Glass Manipulation in Scientific Research," Prentice-Hall, Englewood Cliffs, N. J., 1946.

2. Cold Baths

It is often necessary to cool an apparatus or container below room temperature. This is usually accomplished by submerging the apparatus or container in a Dewar containing some suitable cold liquid. The cold baths listed in Table 17.1 are convenient for maintaining the indicated temperatures. The baths listed in bold-face type are useful as secondary standards of temperature.

TABLE 17.1

Cold Baths

Bath	Temperature, °C.
Ice—water slush	**0**
Ice—NaCl soln. slush Ice—HCl soln. slush	0 to −20
Carbon tetrachloride slush[a]	**−22.9**
Liquid ammonia[b]	−33 to −45
Chlorobenzene slush[a]	**−45.2**
Chloroform slush[a]	**−63.5**
Dry ice—cellosolve slush **Dry ice—isopropanol slush** **Dry ice—acetone slush**	**−78.5**[c]

[a] These baths are prepared in the hood by slowly adding liquid nitrogen to the stirred liquids in Dewars until the consistency of a thick malted milk is achieved. Care must be taken that a solid crust does not form or the Dewar may break.

[b] Must be used in a hood or a very well-ventilated room.

[c] The temperature of this bath is a function of the pressure of carbon-dioxide vapor in equilibrium with the dry ice, and hence of atmospheric pressure.

TABLE 17.1 (continued)

Cold Baths

Bath	Temperature, °C.
Ethyl acetate slush[a]	**−83.6**
Toluene slush[a]	−95
Carbon disulfide slush[a]	**−111.6**
Methylcyclohexane slush[a]	**−126.3**
n-Pentane slush[a]	−130
iso-Pentane slush[a]	−160.5
Liquid nitrogen	−196

3. Vapor-pressure Thermometers

One of the most convenient and accurate methods for measuring a low temperature is to measure the vapor pressure of an appropriate substance at the temperature in question. The substance is contained in a small space connected directly to a mercury manometer. The vapor pressures of substances suitable for vapor-pressure thermometers in the range −10° to −182° are given in Table 17.2. Temperatures between −180° and −210°

TABLE 17.2

Vapor Pressure Thermometer Data[3]

(Vapor pressures given in mm. of mercury)

°C	SO_2	°C	SO_2	NH_3	°C	NH_3	CO_2
−10	759.8	−33	242.8	773.7	−56	213.0	
−11	726.6	−34	229.7	736.0	−57	199.9	
−12	694.6	−35	217.1	699.6	−58	187.5	
−13	663.7	−36	205.1	664.6	−59	175.8	
−14	633.9	−37		631.0	−60	164.7	
−15	605.3	−38		598.9	−61	154.2	
−16	577.7	−39		568.2	−62	144.2	
−17	551.0	−40		538.7	−63	134.8	
−18	525.3	−41		510.5	−64	125.9	
−19	500.6	−42		483.5	−65	117.5	
−20	476.7	−43		457.7	−66	109.5	
−21	453.9	−44		433.2	−67	102.0	
−22	432.1	−45		409.7	−68	95.0	
−23	411.2	−46		387.2	−69	88.4	
−24	390.9	−47		365.7	−70	82.2	
−25	371.3	−48		345.2	−71	76.3	
−26	352.6	−49		325.7	−72	70.8	
−27	334.7	−50		307.1	−73	65.6	
−28	317.7	−51		289.4	−74	60.7	
−29	301.4	−52		272.5	−75	56.2	
−30	285.8	−53		256.5	−76	52.0	
−31	270.8	−54		241.3	−77	48.0	860.0
−32	256.5	−55		226.8	−78		792.9

TABLE 17.2 (continued)

°C	CO_2	C_2H_4	°C	C_2H_4	°C	C_2H_4	CH_4
−79	730.5		−114	398.2	−149	16.9	
−80	672.6		−115	371.9	−150	14.9	1720
−81	618.7		−116	347.0	−151		1613
−82	568.4		−117	323.5	−152		1510
−83	521.7		−118	301.3	−153		1412
−84	478.6		−119	280.3	−154		1318
−85	438.7		−120	260.5	−155		1229
−86	401.6		−121	241.9	−156		1145
−87	367.4		−122	224.4	−157		1064
−88	335.8		−123	207.9	−158		988
−89	306.5		−124	192.4	−159		916
−90	279.4		−125	177.8	−160		848
−91	254.5		−126	164.1	−161		783.0
−92	231.7		−127	151.2	−162		722.4
−93	210.7		−128	139.1	−163		663.8
−94	191.4		−129	127.8	−164		609.6
−95	173.7		−130	117.2	−165		559.3
−96	157.4		−131	107.3	−166		512.2
−97	142.5		−132	98.1	−167		468.2
−98	128.8		−133	89.6	−168		427.2
−99	116.3		−134	81.7	−169		388.8
−100	104.9		−135	74.4	−170		353.2
−101	94.5		−136	67.7	−171		320.4
−102	85.0		−137	61.5	−172		290.0
−103	76.3	792.0	−138	55.7	−173		262.0
−104	68.4	747.5	−139	50.4	−174		236.1
−105	61.3	705.1	−140	45.6	−175		212.1
−106	54.8	664.5	−141	41.2	−176		190.0
−107	49.0	625.6	−142	37.1	−177		169.6
−108	43.7	588.4	−143	33.3	−178		151.1
−109		552.8	−144	29.9	−179		134.4
−110		518.8	−145	26.7	−180		118.9
−111		486.3	−146	23.9	−181		105.1
−112		455.4	−147	21.3	−182		92.6
−113		426.0	−148	19.0			

may be determined by measuring the vapor pressure of oxygen or nitrogen, the data for which are given in Sanderson[1] and Dodd and Robinson.[2] The

[1] R. T. Sanderson, "Vacuum Manipulation of Volatile Compounds," John Wiley and Sons, New York, 1948, pp. 120–121.

[2] R. E. Dodd and P. L. Robinson, "Experimental Inorganic Chemistry," Elsevier, New York, 1954, p. 65.

data of Table 17.2 are those of Stock, Henning, and Kuss[3] and have not been corrected to 0°C. = 273.15°K. The uncorrected data are probably good for determining temperatures to $\pm 0.1°C$. For more accurate work, it is suggested that the temperature correction be made and that the more recent literature be consulted.[4]

4. Hygrostats

A saturated aqueous solution in contact with an excess of a solid phase at a given temperature will maintain constant humidity in a closed space. A number of salts suitable for this purpose are listed in Table 17.3.

TABLE 17.3

Vapor Pressures of Saturated Aqueous Solutions[5]

Solid Phase	Vapor Pressure of Water (mm.), 20°C
$Na_2HPO_4 \cdot 12 \, H_2O$	16.7
K_2HPO_4	16.1
$KHSO_4$	15.1
KBr	14.7
$(NH_4)_2SO_4$	14.2
NH_4Cl	13.9
$NH_4Cl + KNO_3$	12.7
$Mg(C_2H_3O_2)_2 \cdot 4 \, H_2O$	11.4
$NaBr \cdot 2 \, H_2O$	10.2
$NaHSO_4 \cdot H_2O$	9.12
$KSCN$	8.24
$Zn(NO_3)_2 \cdot 6 \, H_2O$	7.36
$CaCl_2 \cdot 6 \, H_2O$	5.66
$KC_2H_3O_2$	3.51
$LiCl \cdot H_2O$	2.63

5. Desiccants

Some of the common desiccants, with their approximate gas-drying efficiencies, are listed in Table 17.4.

[3] A. Stock, F. Henning, and E. Kuss, *Ber.*, **54**, 1119 (1921).

[4] For SO_2, see W. F. Giauque and C. C. Stephenson, *J. Am. Chem. Soc.*, **60**, 1389 (1938); for NH_3, see G. T. Armstrong, "A Critical Review of the Literature Relating to the Vapor Pressure of Ammonia and Trideuteroammonia," Nat'l Bureau of Standards Report No. 2626; for CO_2, see W. F. Giauque and C. J. Egan, *J. Chem. Phys.*, **5**, 45 (1937); for C_2H_4, see A. B. Lamb and E. E. Roper, *J. Am. Chem. Soc.*, **62**, 806 (1940).

[5] Calculated from the data in *International Critical Tables*, Vol. I, McGraw-Hill, New York, 1926, pp. 67–68.

TABLE 17.4

The Efficiencies of Desiccants

Desiccant	Residual Water (P_{mm} or mg./l.)
Efficient trap at $-196°$	10^{-23}
CaH_2	$< 10^{-5}$
Efficient trap at $-100°$	1×10^{-5}
P_2O_5	2×10^{-5}
$Mg(ClO_4)_2$	5×10^{-4}
Efficient trap at $-78°$	5×10^{-4}
BaO	7×10^{-4}
Linde Molecular Sieves	0.001
SiO_2 gel; active Al_2O_3; KOH	~ 0.002
$CaSO_4$	0.005
CaO; 96% H_2SO_4	~ 0.01
$CaCl_2$	~ 0.2

6. Compressed-gas Cylinders

Many gases can be bought compressed in cylinders. Unfortunately, there is very little standardization as to type of valve outlet and cylinder color. Some of the common compressed gases and recommended fittings are listed in Table 17.5. Chemical supply house catalogs should be consulted for alternate fittings and for lists of other gases which are available.

In most laboratory applications, gases are bled from cylinders into systems which are near atmospheric pressure and are provided with some sort of safety outlet in case too high a pressure is reached. The main valve of a cylinder cannot be used for bleeding gas into such a system, inasmuch as this valve is simply an on-or-off valve. A needle valve (See Figure 17.5) must be connected to the cylinder in order to control the flow of gas. With this arrangement, the main cylinder valve must never be opened unless the needle valve is closed. After opening the main valve, the needle valve is opened sufficiently to obtain the desired flow rate. This arrangement is unsatisfactory for gases whose critical points are below room temperature because, as the cylinder pressure falls, the needle valve needs frequent adjustment in order to maintain a constant flow rate. For these gases, one should interpose an automatic pressure regulator (see Figure 17.5) between the cylinder and the needle valve. The automatic regulator is used to reduce the cylinder pressure

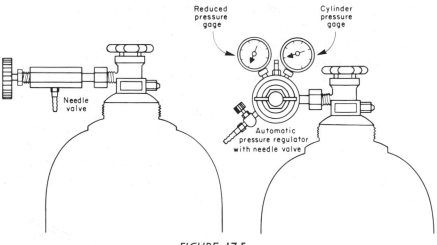

FIGURE 17.5.

Compressed-gas controllers.

to the range 5–50 p.s.i. This control pressure will remain essentially constant, despite a drop in cylinder pressure. One should never use an automatic regulator without a needle valve.

TABLE 17.5

Fittings for Gas Cylinders

Substance	*Cylinder Valve Outlet*	*Recommended Control*	*Full Cylinder Pressure* (P.S.I.G., 70°F)
A, He, N₂ (water pumped)	.965″ RH INT (accepting bullet-shaped nipple)	Automatic Pressure Regulator plus Needle Valve	1600–2200
A, He, N₂ (oil pumped)	.965″ LH INT (accepting bullet-shaped nipple)	Automatic Pressure Regulator plus Needle Valve	1600–2200
H₂, CO	.825″ LH EXT (accepting round nipple)	Automatic Pressure Regulator plus Needle Valve	1600–2000, 800–1000
O₂	.903″ RH EXT (accepting round nipple)	Automatic Pressure Regulator plus Needle Valve	1600–2200
Cl₂, SO₂	1.030″ RH EXT (flat seat)	Needle Valve (Monel, Brass)	84, 35
CO₂	.825″ RH EXT (flat seat)	Brass Needle Valve	830
HCl	.825″ LH EXT (flat seat)	Monel Needle Valve	613
NH₃	3/8″ RH INT IPS	Steel Needle Valve	114

Many gases may be purchased in "lecture bottles" ($2'' \times 15''$ cylinders) which require special needle-valve fittings. These bottles are recommended whenever small amounts of gases are required.

Most large ammonia cylinders have a "dip pipe" running from the base of the valve to the inside cylinder wall near the shoulder of the cylinder. To withdraw *gas* from the cylinder, it is kept standing upright; but to withdraw *liquid* ammonia, the cylinder must be placed so that its dip pipe is immersed in the liquid. To do this, lay the cylinder down with the butt end about two inches higher than the valve end. The dip pipe will be immersed when the main valve outlet points up. The liquid is generally withdrawn into an un-silvered Dewar so that the rate of withdrawal may be readily observed. See Figure 17.6 for a sketch of a typical set-up.

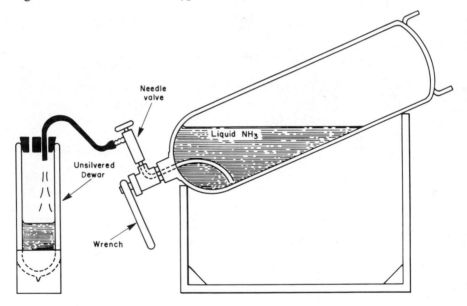

FIGURE 17.6.
Withdrawing liquid ammonia from a cylinder.

7. Dry Sources of Gases

Few laboratories are stocked with more than a dozen kinds of compressed gases. When the occasional need arises for a gas which is not readily available, it is best to prepare such a gas in the laboratory. Directions for the preparation and purification of various gases are described in the literature.[6]

[6] See, for example, R. E. Dodd and P. L. Robinson, "Experimental Inorganic Chemistry." Elsevier, New York, 1954, Chapter 3; or A. Farkas and H. W. Melville, "Experimental Methods in Gas Reactions," Macmillan, London, 1939, Chapter 3.

Certain gases may be very conveniently prepared in small amounts by simply heating certain solids. The latter technique is particularly useful in vacuum-line work. A list of gases and the solids which are heated to produce them is given in Table 17.6.

TABLE 17.6

Dry Sources of Gases

Gas	*Material to be Heated*
O_2	$KMnO_4$, HgO, PbO_2, $KClO_3$, or $K_2Cr_2O_7$
N_2	$(NH_4)_2Cr_2O_7$ or NaN_3
N_2O	NH_4NO_3
NO	intimate mixture of 63.8 g. KNO_2, 25.2 g. KNO_3, 76 g. Cr_2O_3, and 120 g. Fe_2O_3
SO_3	$Fe_2(SO_4)_3$
BF_3	$CaF(BF_4)$ or $B_2O_3 + KBF_4$
H_2	UH_3
$H_2S(H_2Se)$	$S(Se)$ + paraffin wax
CO_2	dry ice, $MgCO_3$, or $NaHCO_3(+H_2O)$
$(CN)_2$	$Hg(CN)_2$
SO_2	$Na_2S_2O_5$
Cl_2	$CuCl_2$

8. *Theoretical Plates and the Binomial Expansion*

Many processes involving the distribution of a chemical species between two phases may be discussed in terms of theoretical plates. Let us consider the situation in which one phase moves in a stepwise manner through a series of batch equilibrations, or plates, in each of which equilibrium is established between the two phases.

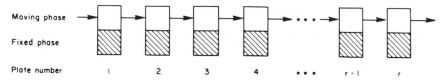

The concentrations of the chemical species in the two phases are related by the distribution coefficient

$$K = C_M/C_F \tag{17.1}$$

where C_M and C_F are the concentrations in the moving and fixed phases, respectively. Hence the fraction f of a species in the moving phase during any equilibration is given by

$$f = \frac{1}{1 + V_F/V_M K} \tag{17.2}$$

where V_F and V_M are the volumes of the fixed and moving phases, respectively, in each plate. After one transfer (the moving phase has advanced to plate 2) the first plate will contain the fraction $1 - f$ of the species and the second plate will contain the fraction f of the species. After two transfers the first plate will contain $(1 - f)^2$ of the species, the second plate will contain $2f(1 - f)$ of the species, and the third plate will contain f^2 of the species. It will be noted that the fraction in the rth plate is the rth term of the binomial expansion of

$$[(1 - f) + f]^n = 1 \qquad (17.3)$$

where n is the number of transfers. The general formula for the fraction in the rth plate after n transfers is

$$F_{n,r} = \frac{n!}{(r - 1)!(n - r + 1)!} f^{r-1}(1 - f)^{n-r+1} \qquad (17.4)$$

It will be noted that $r \leqslant n + 1$. $F_{n,r}$ has a maximum value when $n = r/f$. The distribution of concentrations about the maximum value will be symmetrical (Gaussian) when r, n, and $n - r$ are large. This distribution is given by the equation

$$F_{n,r} = \frac{1}{\sqrt{2\pi r}} e^{-f^2(n-r/f)^2/2r} \qquad (17.5)$$

The maximum value of $F_{n,r}$ is $1/\sqrt{2\pi r}$.

It should be emphasized that the above treatment assumes the constancy of the distribution coefficient (equation 17.1). In actual practice, this coefficient is more or less a function of the concentration of the chemical species undergoing distribution and even of the concentrations of other species. Hence the binomial expansion treatment is only a rough approximation.

9. Locker Equipment

1 Fisher burner, with tubing
1 Chromel triangle
1 wire gauze
2 iron extension rings (3 in.; 4 in.)
1 iron support
2 extension clamps with asbestos-covered jaws
2 extension clamps with three-prong, asbestos-covered jaws
4 clamp holders
2 boxes of matches

1 test-tube rack
10 test tubes (20 × 150 mm.)
1 test-tube holder

7 beakers (1—100, 1—250, 1—400, 1—600, 2—800, 1—1500 ml.)
4 glass rods (2—7 × 280 mm., 2—6 × 180 mm.)
4 Erlenmeyer flasks (1—125, 2—250, 1—500 ml.)
5 watch glasses (2—75, 2—100, 1—150 mm.)
1 polyethylene squeeze bottle, for water (500 ml.)
3 glass-stoppered bottles (1—125, 1—250, 1—500 ml.)
1 weighing bottle (30 ml.)

2 burets (50 ml.)
1 buret holder
1 buret reader
2 graduated cylinders (1—50, 1—250 ml.)
1 volumetric flask (250 ml.)
1 pipet (25 ml.)
1 graduated pipet (5 ml.)
1 filtering funnel with short stem (90 mm.)
1 cylindrical dropping funnel (125 ml.)
1 pear-shape separatory funnel (500 ml.)
2 fritted-glass crucibles (15 ml.)
1 fritted-glass funnel (6 cm.)
1 neoprene filter adapter (for fritted-glass crucibles and funnel)
1 filter flask (500 ml.)
1 filter trap, equipped

2 evaporating dishes (10 and 12 cm.)
4 porcelain crucibles with covers (2—10, 2—50 ml.)
1 iron crucible (50 ml.)
1 pair of crucible tongs

1 round-bottomed flask with three necks (1000 ml.)
1 distilling flask (250 ml.)
1 condenser (30 cm.)
1 adapter

2 thermometers (−10–110°; −10–360°)
1 mortar and pestle (10 cm.)
1 file
1 pair of safety goggles
1 desiccator
1 "Scoopula"
1 Monel spatula
2 towels
1 test-tube brush
1 bottle brush
  rubber tubing (3 ft. suction; 3 ft. regular)

INDEX

CONCENTRATIONS OF COMMERCIAL REAGENTS

Reagent	Density	Weight %	Molarity
Acetic acid	1.05	100%	17.5
Aqueous ammonia	0.90	28	15
Hydriodic acid	1.5	47	5.5
Hydrobromic acid	1.5	48	9
Hydrochloric acid	1.19	37	12
Hydrofluoric acid	1.15	48	28
Hydrogen peroxide	1.11	30	10
Nitric acid	1.42	69	16
Perchloric acid	1.69	72	12
Phosphoric acid	1.69	85	14.5
Sulfuric acid	1.84	96	18